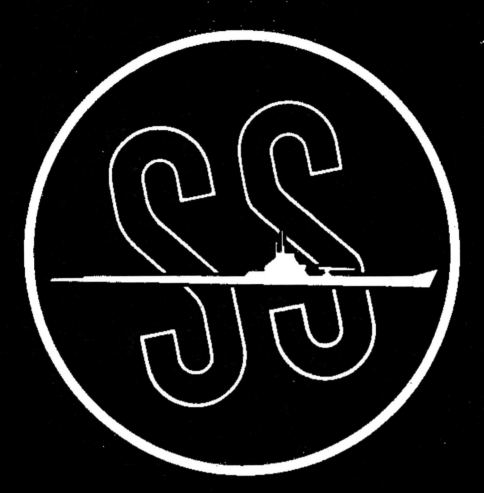

Submarine
Distilling
Systems

NAVPERS 16170

NavPers 16170

Produced for ComSubLant by
Standards and Curriculum Branch,
Training Division, Bureau of Naval Personnel

SUBMARINE

DISTILLING

SYSTEMS

Revised: January 1955

ISBN # 978-1-935327-01-1 1-935327-01-1

*This is one of a series of Submarine
Training Manuals. The series includes:*

PREFACE

This manual has been revised by the U. S. Naval Submarine School, New London, Connecticut. It is designed as both an instruction and a service manual covering the established procedures for the operation and maintenance of the distilling equipment used on a modern submarine.

The manual includes a description of the uses to which distilled water is put in a submarine.

The Model S and the Model X-1 distilling systems are described in full detail. Relative instructions for operation, maintenance, inspections and repairs for distilling plants with alterations and conversions and repairs are included. Separate chapters covering the operation and the care and maintenance of each system are included. Detailed descriptive information is given on starting and stopping procedures, installation and repair techniques, and inspection routines. Free use is made of job sheets outlining in chronological order the steps necessary for the successful completion of the more common maintenance and service conditions. Newly constructed submarines use various designs of distilling plants which will be mentioned briefly in text.

CONTENTS

ILLUSTRATIONS

1

DISTILLATION OF SEA WATER

A. FRESH WATER

1A1. Importance of fresh water. Fresh water has always been a major item aboard ship; in fact, until comparatively recent times it has been the factor that controlled the length of time a ship could remain at sea. In the era of sailing ships, it was necessary to spread canvas whenever it rained, and to catch the rain water in canvas water monkey bags in order to replenish the supply of fresh water on board. This water was used only for cooking and drinking purposes, there being no need then for fresh water in the operation of steam-driven propulsion machinery.

On modern naval vessels fresh water is of even more importance, for it is used not only for cooking, drinking and bathing, but also in boilers, storage batteries, and as a cooling agent for modern Diesel engines. All large naval vessels have distilling plants operated by steam, either high or low pressure, which vary in capacity and type with the size and class of ship.

1A2. Submarine sea water distillers. The first successful apparatus for distilling sea water on submarines was the Nelseco-Clarkson exhaust evaporator installed about 1916. This evaporator operated by using the exhaust from the main engines to heat the water to the boiling point, and as the salt water boiled, the vapor was led to a condenser where it condensed to fresh water. Since the operating conditions of the engine varied, the heat value of exhaust gas available varied accordingly, and hence it was almost impossible to maintain a heat balance. The quantity and quality of the fresh water varied with the operating conditions. The disadvantage of this evaporator for submarine use was that it could be operated only at full capacity when the submarine was running on the surface at high speeds. It could not be used during periods of submergence.

During the period from 1937 to 1940 a vapor compression type of distilling unit was developed for use aboard submarines. Experiments on this unit were conducted under actual operating con-

ditions on board the submarine U. S. S. S-20 at New London, Connecticut, and resulted in the development of the electrically operated Model S vapor compression distilling unit which produces 750 gallons per day (gpd). These units were installed on all new submarines and were used to replace the Nelseco-Clarkson type on older submarines.

Further experiments with distilling units were conducted by the manufacturer in coordination with the Bureau of Ships and in 1943, the Model X (1,000 and 2,000 gpd) vapor compression distilling unit was developed. The Model X-1 (1,000 gpd) distilling units were, for a number of years, the only units to be installed on new submarines.

During the interval from that time until the present (Jan. 1955), a number of improvements and alterations have been made to the original Model X-1 installations. The two-lobed compressors have been replaced with General Motors three-lobed compressors. (Section 7B) The original heat exchangers, in which there were three small tubes inside of each larger tube, have been replaced with the improved type described in this text. The designation of the improved distilling units was changed from Model X-1 to Model AAA-1.

In this text, frequent reference is made to the Model X-1 distilling unit. It is to be understood, unless specifically stated otherwise, that each reference applies also to the Model AAA-1 unit.

Further alterations have been made to adapt the units to snorkeling conditions. It may be expected that the designation of these converted units may be changed again.

There are also several newer models of distilling plants undergoing service tests on some of the later types of submarines. These new models will be described briefly in Chapter 10.

1A3. Submarine distilling equipment. The distilling plants in use on submarines consist of: the

Kleinschmidt, Model S; the Badger Models X–1, Y–1, V 1, WS–1, the Cleaver-Brooks 300 gpd, and the Griscom-Russell 4,000 gpd Soloshell installed on Nautilus. There are two (2) units of each applicable type installed on all of the later class vessels except the SST's, the SSK's, and the SSN's which have only one (1) unit. The Models are described and illustrated separately.

1A4. Consumption of fresh water.

A modern submarine consumes during a war patrol an average of approximately 500 gallons per day of fresh water for cooking, drinking, washing and engine makeup water. In addition to this consumption the main storage batteries require about 500 gallons of battery water per week; giving a total requirement of at least 4,000 gallons per week. These minimum requirements will leave enough water for each man in the crew to have a bath at least twice a week.

1A5. Fresh water stowage capacity.

The normal fresh water stowage capacity on most submarines is about 5,600 gallons; of this, 1,200 gallons are battery water and are stored in the battery water tanks. This water will last only about ten days, and it is good practice not to allow the fresh water supply on hand to drop below one-half the normal capacity.

The operation of the submarine itself determines when the distilling plant should be used. On some vessels, the auxiliary tanks are filled with fresh water prior to leaving the tender or base. This water is used for showers and washing of clothes and supplements the normal capacity.

Small fresh water tanks are located in the forward and after compartments and contain emergency fresh water, but this supply is held in reserve and is not normally used.

2

DESCRIPTION OF THE
MODEL S DISTILLING UNIT

A. PRINCIPLES OF DISTILLING ACTION

2A1. What is distillation? A ship is always surrounded by limitless quantities of water, except when in drydock; but this is sea water, unfit for human consumption or use in the batteries. If the salt and other substances in sea water could be removed there would be sufficient pure water at hand for all purposes. Such substances can be removed by distillation. The knowledge of distilling liquids comes from ancient days. Distillation is simply the boiling of a liquid and the condensing of its vapor back to the liquid state again. If a teaspoon is held in a cloud of steam rising from a teakettle, the vapor will condense on the spoon and the resulting liquid is distilled water. In the boiling most or all of the impurities are left behind, so that the condensed liquid is relatively pure.

2A2. Purifying action of distillation. Salt and other substances are dissolved, or in solution, in sea water. Sea water does not boil at the same temperature as does fresh water (212° F., at sea level pressure), but at a temperature a few degrees higher. When sea water boils, it is only the water that is vaporized at this temperature, and if this pure vapor is led into another clean container where it may condense, the condensate is pure distilled water. The salt (sodium chloride) and other solid ingredients in the sea water do not vaporize and hence do not appear in the distilled water.

2A3. General explanation of distillation. Figure 2–1 shows a cutaway view of the Model S distilling unit in full detail. Figure 2–2 shows a highly simplified schematic diagram of the working parts of the distilling unit, with arrows indicating the flow of the water and vapor through it.

The distilling process in the Model S distilling unit is a continuous one; sea water is supplied at the rate of about a gallon a minute; part of this is turned to distilled water; the solid residue and concentrated brine flow out separately from the distilled water.

Inside a casing, a long length of tubing is coiled into a cone, set with its small end down. There are ten such cones nested together. Cold sea water enters at the bottom between the cones, that is, it flows around the *outside* of the tubing. On its way upward it is heated, so that it is boiling when it emerges from between the cones at the upper end. The vapor is led through a vapor separator into a compressor, where it is compressed and is then discharged down into the *inside* of the tubing. On the way down through the tubing this vapor is gradually cooled by contact with the colder tubing walls, finally condensing therein and flowing out as pure distilled water to a storage tank. The nested cones of tubing therefore act as *heat exchangers*. The distilled water is technically known as *distillate* or *condensate*. The path of this flow may be easily seen in Figure 2–2.

2A4. Necessity for compressing the vapor. The question may be raised as to why the vapor is compressed in the distilling unit. The explanation involves several considerations, as follows:

The conical nest of tubes serves four purposes: (1) to heat the feed water, (2) to generate the vapor, (3) to condense the vapor, and (4) to cool the condensate to a lower temperature. In the lower part of the nest, the feed water is at the temperature of sea water; the temperature increases during the upward flow, and the feed water leaves the nest boiling. On the downward flow, the vapor is condensed in the upper part of the tube nest, and hot condensed liquid is cooled in the lower part of the tube nest.

Since sea water does not boil at the same temperature, for a given pressure, as does fresh water, but at several degrees higher, the feed water in the upper part of the nest is actually above 212° F. The vapor from the boiling water is no longer sea water, but fresh water vapor. Fresh water vapor at atmospheric pressure condenses only at 212° F. When a vapor is compressed, its boiling

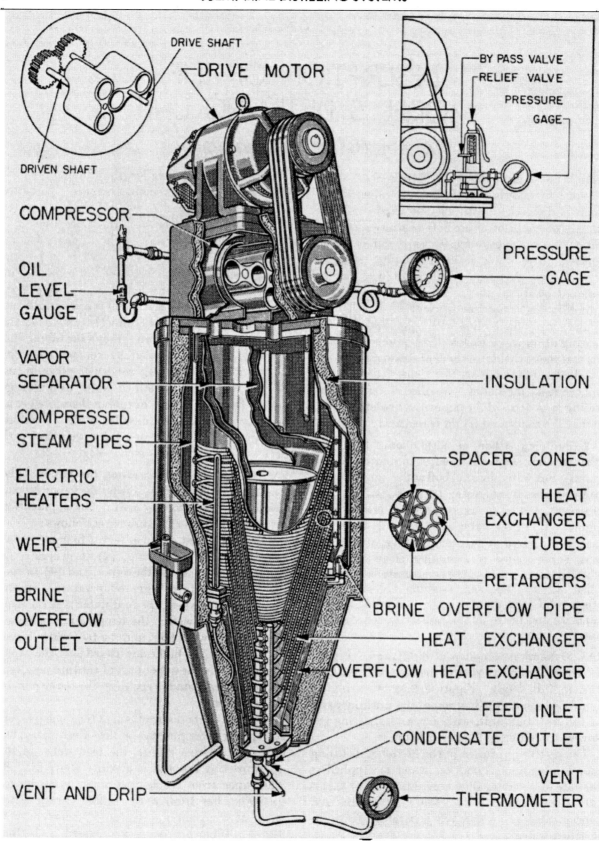

Figure 2-1. Model S distilling unit (cutaway view).

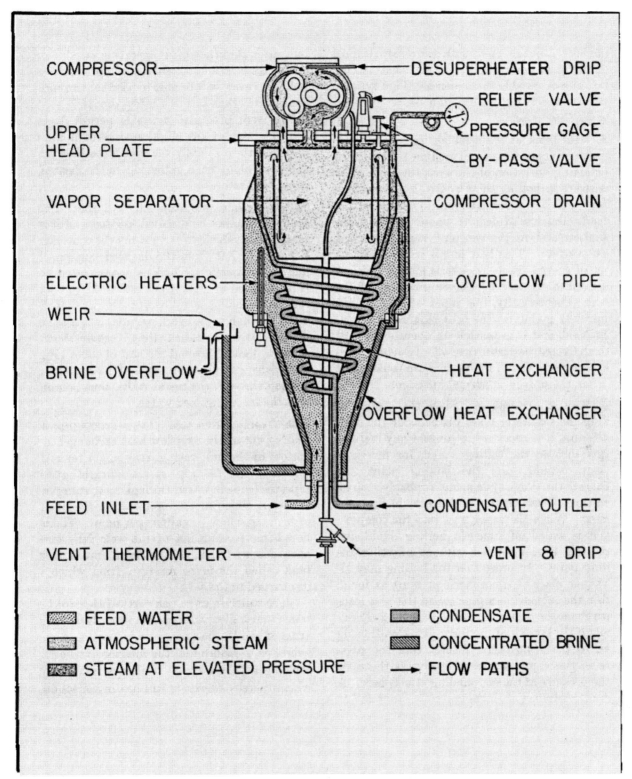

COMPRESSOR

DESUPERHEATER DRIP

RELIEF VALVE

PRESSURE GAGE

BY-PASS VALVE

UPPER
HEAD PLATE

VAPOR SEPARATOR

COMPRESSOR DRAIN

ELECTRIC HEATERS

OVERFLOW PIPE

WEIR

BRINE OVERFLOW

HEAT EXCHANGER

OVERFLOW HEAT EXCHANGER

FEED INLET

CONDENSATE OUTLET

VENT THERMOMETER

VENT & DRIP

FEED WATER
ATMOSPHERIC STEAM
STEAM AT ELEVATED PRESSURE

CONDENSATE
CONCENTRATED BRINE
FLOW PATHS

Figure 2-2.   Model S distilling unit (schematic view).

point or its condensation point is raised above the temperature of the hot feed water in the upper part of the tube nest. Thus, when the compressed vapor enters the nest on its path downward, it finds a temperature lower than its new condensation point, and so is able to condense. This type of apparatus accordingly is called a *vapor compression distilling unit*.

2A5. Heat input of the distilling unit. The compression of vapor serves still another purpose. In the starting operation of the unit, the feed water is raised to its boiling point by the electric heaters. After the unit is in normal operation, there will be a steady heat loss of definite amount through the insulation and in the outgoing condensate and brine overflow. This heat loss is balanced by an input of energy from the electric motor, which is transformed to heat by the compression of the vapor. Theoretically, this input of heat by the compressor maintains the heat balance at a constant level, and it is possible to operate the unit with all electric heaters turned off. In actual practice, however, some of the heaters are usually left on after the unit is in normal operation.

2A6. Vent to atmosphere. Since the process of boiling the sea water takes place inside the shell of the unit, it is necessary to prevent any increase of pressure on the boiling water, for increased pressure would raise the boiling point and unbalance the whole system, and probably stop its operation. The situation is different in the compressor. When the vapor goes into the compressor, it is sealed off from the boiling liquid and may then be compressed without affecting the boiling point. In order that the boiling may always take place at atmospheric pressure as found within the submarine, a pipe called the *vent* leads down from the *vapor separator* (Figure 2–2) out through the bottom of the unit. This vent, being open to the atmosphere, insures that the pressure in the vapor separator is always the same as the pressure of the surrounding atmosphere. A distant reading dial thermometer is connected to the vent by a flexible tubing and gives the temperature in the vent pipe.

Although this open vent pipe leads downward out of the unit, the steam will not flow out when in normal amount inside, because the outer atmosphere exerts pressure upon it through the vent. However the interior and exterior pressures are so

maintained that there is a very small excess of pressure inside the unit, which causes a slight feather of steam to appear at the vent. This is an indication that the unit is operating satisfactorily. Any excess steam which the compressor cannot hold, however, will be able to pass out through the vent, which thus acts as a safety device.

This vent pipe also serves to permit drainage into the bilge of any slight amount of liquid carried into the vapor by the violent boiling action, and prevents it from gathering on the floor of the vapor separator.

2A7. Sea water not distilled. All the incoming sea water cannot be distilled, for some of it must remain as a vehicle to carry away the concentrated salt content left from the distilled portion. The undistilled portion, which is concentrated brine, is maintained at a level just above the top coil of the heat exchanger by overflow pipes. It flows down through these overflow pipes into a separate conical passage, called the *overflow heat exchanger*, located around the nest of tubes (Figure 2–2), where it gives up some of its heat by conduction through the metal walls, thus helping to heat the incoming feed water.

2A8. Overflow weir cup. The overflow pipe after leading out of the overflow heat exchanger at the bottom of the unit casing, rises again for a short distance. At the top of the upright overflow pipe, the brine flows out through an opening called the *weir*, which meters or measures the quantity of brine overflow in gallons per hour. The overflow brine passing out of the weir falls into an open cup and then drains down into a storage tank called the *brine receiver*, from which it is discharged to the sea.

Since water in any open vertical U-shaped container must always be at the same level in both arms of the U, the open weir is located at such a height as to insure that the interior overflow heat exchanger (Figure 2–2) is always full of liquid, which thereby exerts its full heating effect on the sea water inside.

2A9. Time required to start sea water boiling in the distilling unit. When starting the unit, it takes from 60 to 90 minutes to bring the sea water to the boiling point.

2A10. Heat balance in the distilling unit. It is important to know the heat flow through the vari-

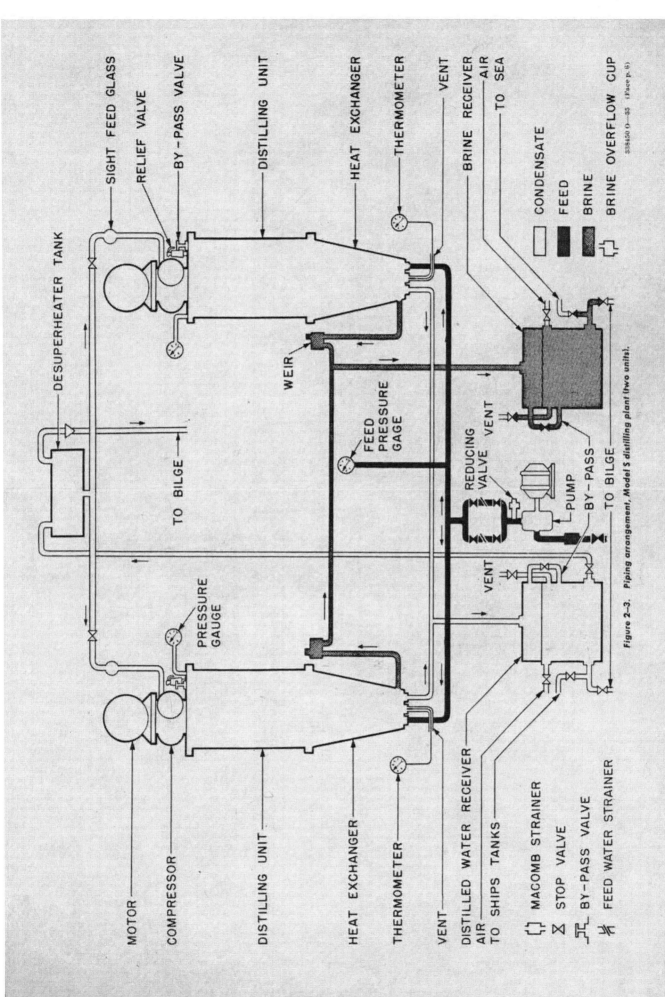

SIGHT FEED GLASS

RELIEF VALVE

BY-PASS VALVE

DISTILLING UNIT

HEAT EXCHANGER

THERMOMETER

VENT

BRINE RECEIVER
AIR
TO SEA

CONDENSATE

FEED

BRINE

BRINE OVERFLOW CUP

DESUPERHEATER TANK

TO BILGE

WEIR

FEED PRESSURE GAGE

REDUCING VALVE VENT

PUMP

BY-PASS

TO BILGE

VENT

PRESSURE GAUGE

MOTOR

COMPRESSOR

DISTILLING UNIT

HEAT EXCHANGER

THERMOMETER

VENT

DISTILLED WATER RECEIVER
AIR
TO SHIPS TANKS

MACOMB STRAINER

STOP VALVE

BY-PASS VALVE

FEED WATER STRAINER

S38450 O—65   (Face p. 6)

Figure 2—3.   Piping arrangement, Model S distilling plant (two units).

ous parts of the unit in actual quantities. The following example is typical.

Heat input. The total input of heat is 16,125 Btu per hour, when the unit is fully operating with 10,185 Btu per hour from the compressor and 5,940 Btu per hour from the electric heaters.

Heat loss. The total quantity of heat loss that flows out through the four separate paths, is as follows:

  1,825 Btu per hour in the condensate.
 11,600 Btu per hour in the overflow.
    400 Btu per hour through the vent.
  2,300 Btu per hour by radiation from hot metal parts.

This represents a total heat loss of 16,125 Btu per hour. The heat balance is not always at this exact number of Btu per hour, because various momentary changes of rate of feed and temperature of sea water, voltage fluctuations in the motor, and other operating conditions, naturally will cause it to shift around.

The heat balance of the unit is very sensitive and all changes which may be necessary in the operating conditions should be made slowly.

2A11. Purity of distilled water. If no leaks are present in the system, the distilled water will contain not over four parts of salt to a million parts of water. The distiller cannot, of course, remove any volatile liquids, that is, liquids which boil at or below the boiling temperature of water. For example, in badly polluted harbors or streams, a trace of ammonia may be present in the distilled water; and in improperly chlorinated waters, a trace of chlorine may likewise come over in the distilled water.

2A12. Two-unit plant. In the complete submarine distilling plant there are two separate units, each with its necessary control devices, connected in parallel. They are normally operated at the same time, not alternately. A schematic diagram of the complete system, with piping connections, valves, and tanks is shown in Figure 2–3.

Two units are necessary, not only as a safety factor, but also to provide sufficient distilled water. These units may normally be run 300 to 350 operating hours without cleaning, each giving 40 gallons per hour. This means a total of 24,000 to 28,000 gallons of distilled water. The consumption of distilled water is about 500 gallons per day

for all purposes. On a war patrol lasting 60 days, the total consumption will be about 30,000 gallons, and may run higher in the tropics.

2A13. Water for storage batteries. Water distilled from sea water is entirely fit for human consumption and for storage batteries. In the event fresh water is taken aboard from shore, such fresh water has to be distilled before it is suitable for storage battery use. Only fresh water taken aboard at a United States port and definitely known to be pure may be used without distilling or boiling for drinking, cooking, or other human use. In distilling fresh water that may be taken aboard, the operation of the distilling unit is practically the same as when distilling sea water; the only difference being that the overflow is returned to the ship's fresh water tanks from the brine tank, instead of being discharged overboard.

2A14. Testing storage battery water. Water that has been distilled must be tested for purity before it is used in the storage batteries.

a. *Test for purity.* The instrument used to make this test is the Kleinschmidt Water Tester, Type No. A. It is self-contained in a box 6 x 6 x 4¾ inches, operated by three flashlight cells. A small open top container, called a cell, has two fine platinum wire electrodes inside, which lead through the base of the container to prongs. When these prongs are inserted in the socket, the electrodes become part of the electrical circuit. The metered scale is graduated from 0 to 100 in microamperes. A reading of 40 microamperes indicates that the water contains 0.29 grains of salt per gallon. Any reading above 40 shows that the water contains too much salt for storage battery purposes. Detailed instructions for using the tester follow:

CAUTION. Do not touch the inside of the cell for any reason. To do so will contaminate the surfaces and may ruin the fine platinum electrodes in the cell. Clean only by rinsing with the liquid to be tested.

1. Set switch (beneath the meter) to CHECK and turn knob (lower right) until the meter reads 50 (red line). Then turn the switch to the READ position.

2. Remove the cell and remove the cell cover; rinse the cell and fill it with the water to be tested.

3. *Do not* replace the cell cover while the cell is full of water. The testing should be conducted

without the cover in place. The cell cover should be in place only when the cell is empty and not in use.

4. Wipe moisture from the outside of the cell, particularly the prongs in the base, with a *clean* cloth. Care should be taken to prevent the cloth or anything else from coming in contact with the water in the cell being tested.

5. Insert the cell in the socket carefully so as not to spill any water, and read the meter immediately. Do not wait for the meter needle to steady since it may drift either up or down from the correct initial reading.

6. The Model S distilling unit, when working properly, will produce water having a reading between 10 and 20. Water giving readings less than 40 is suitable for use in storage batteries; however, readings as high as 40 indicate that leakage is occurring within the still.

7. If a reading is obtained which indicates contaminated water, this should not be taken as the final test. Five or six check tests should be run to make sure the water itself and not the tester is faulty.

8. The tester serves to protect the batteries against an excess of sodium chloride and thereby serves to indicate whether the distillate is being contaminated by sea water. It will not protect against an excess of iron, copper, or nickel. Samples of battery water should be given a complete chemical analysis to determine conformity to the Bureau of Ships instructions when shore testing facilities are available.

9. The tester is shipped from the factory without the flashlight cells necessary for its operation. Three Navy Type O flashlight cells should be installed for operation. If the tester is to be stored for any length of time, especially in tropical climates, the flashlight cells should be removed from the tester.

10. When check readings cannot be adjusted to 50, the flashlight cells should be renewed.

b. *Silver nitrate test.* Silver nitrate is sometimes used as a quick test of the condensate. Pour some of the condensate in a glass. Drop in a few drops of silver nitrate solution or a small crystal of silver nitrate. If the water remains perfectly clear, it is safe for storage battery use. If any cloudiness or precipitate shows, the water is not fit for storage battery use.

3

MECHANICAL DETAILS OF MODEL S DISTILLING UNIT

A. GENERAL DESCRIPTION

3A1. Main parts. The Model S distilling unit consists of eight main elements: *insulation, shell, heat exchanger, vapor separator, overflow heat exchanger, compressor, motor,* and *variable pitch drive.*

3A2. Insulation. Because of the delicate heat balance on which the unit operates, the *insulation* must be very efficient, so that as much of the heat as possible may be retained inside the unit to do its proper work.

The whole apparatus, with the exception of the motor and variable pitch drive, is covered with a 2-inch layer of glass wool insulation. This insulation is attached to stainless steel jackets, which form the outer casing of the unit. The jackets with insulation are held in place by clamps and are readily removable.

3A3. Shell. Inside the jacket and insulation is the *shell,* against which the insulation makes contact. This copper nickel shell encloses only the heat exchanger and vapor separator. It consists of two parts, the cylindrical upper part and the conical lower part; the two parts are bolted together. The upper shell is bolted to the upper head plate, which is the main support of the whole unit. The lower part of the shell consists of two nested conical sections 3/16-inch apart, bolted at the bottom to the lower head plate. The space between these two lower conical sections forms the overflow heat exchanger (Figure 2–2).

3A4. Heat exchanger. Within the lower conical portion of the shell lies the main *heat exchanger,* projecting part way up into the upper cylindrical portion. The heat exchanger consists of ten cones of copper nickel tubing, nested together and pointed downward. Each cone is made up of eight lengths of 1/4-inch o.d. copper-nickel tubing. Each piece of tubing is 44 inches long. The tubes are wound very tightly against each other in parallel on a cone shaped mandrel. They are tack-

brazed to prevent their unwinding. The cones measure about 4 inches in diameter at the bottom, 19 inches in diameter at the top, and are a little over 2 feet high. The upper ends of the tubes are connected by unions to eight upper headers placed vertically, and attached to the upper head plate. The lower ends of the tubes in each cone are brazed to a small coil header, horizontally placed, connected by unions to a single lower discharge header.

3A5. Retarders. A 1/8-inch square metal rod is inserted into the lower two-thirds portion of each tube. These rods are called *retarders,* and serve to decrease the inner area of the tubes through this section so that most of the condensate comes in contact with the walls of the tubes, thereby obtaining maximum heat transfer. The retarders also limit the flow of steam through the tubes, thus maintaining proper compressor discharge pressure (see Figure 2–1).

3A6. Nesting of coils. Five of the ten cones of tubing are wound right hand and five left hand. They are alternated in the assembly.

Between the cones of tubes there are assembled three sheet metal cone spacers made of copper nickel, .020 inch thick. These metal spacers are inserted to form a seal between the cones of tubing. Three are used to provide sufficient flexibility to form a contour to fit the tube cones tightly. If only one spacer were used it would have to be of such thickness that it would require machining to make a tight seal. These spacer cones, acting as seals, insure that the feed water travels around the small passages that exist between the tubes and the spacer cones (Figure 2–1). Having the cone shaped coils wound both left and right and installed alternately prevents their interlocking when forced tightly together. Inside the inner cone of tubes there is another sheet metal cone, the inside of which is sealed off and has no working purpose. The upper plate of this cone is the floor of the vapor separator. The vent pipe passes out through the bottom of this cone.

3A7. Feed water flow. The incoming water enters from the single feed inlet pipe to the triangular spacers between the tubing and spacers and flows up through a path about 30 feet long before it emerges at the top. During this flow, heat transfer takes place by conduction through the walls of the tubing, (a) heating the feed water gradually to boiling, (b) vaporizing two-thirds of it, (c) condensing the vapor from the compressor, and (d) cooling the condensed liquid.

3A8. Electric heaters. The heat exchanger projects part way up into the upper cylindrical portion of the shell. Here, between the cones of tubes and the shell, is a narrow space into which the water, now at the boiling point, enters (Figure 2-2). The eight electric heaters, spaced equally around the shell, extend into this space. The water level is maintained above the tops of these heaters.

The heaters are 500 watts, 125 volts special chromalox immersion type, of hairpin design (Figure 3-1). They measure 17⅝ inches over-all in length; 14 inches immersion length; 12⅝ inches active heating length. Two heaters are wired in series to each switch, requiring four heater switches. Replacement heaters are carried in the spare parts box, with a special wrench for removing and installing them.

CAUTION. The electric heaters should be turned on only when submerged as they will *burn out* unless covered with water. The large quantity of heat produced is safely carried away by the surrounding water.

3A9. The vapor separator. The *vapor separator* is enclosed by an open cylinder extending downward from the upper head plate. This cylinder is concentric and inside another open end cylinder extending upward from the conical shaped filler for the heat exchanger. The floor of the separator is formed by the bottom of the outer cylinder and lies about 4½ inches below the topmost coil of the heat exchanger. The vapor separator is thus a separate enclosed chamber. The vapor from the boiling water rises in the narrow space between the shell and the outer separator wall; it then descends between the walls, and enters the separator

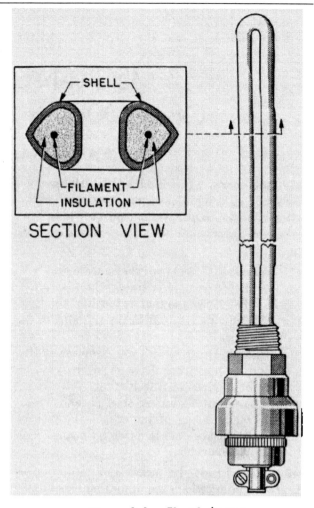

Figure 3-1.   Electric heater.

chamber. This circuitous passage of the vapor causes any mist of liquid that may be carried up by the vigorous boiling action to *separate* from the vapor; hence the name—separator. Such liquid will of course not be distilled, and must be prevented from entering the vapor compressor or it will contaminate the distilled water. The separated liquid collects on the separator floor and drains out through the vent pipe.

3A10. Vapor baffle. On entering the separator, the vapor first strikes against a *baffle*. This baffle, cylindrical in shape, is attached at the top to the upper head plates. It extends to 1 inch above the separator floor and is located 1 inch inside the outer separator wall. This arrangement insures that the vapor, after passing through the narrow inlet opening at the top, passes down and through the free end of the baffle and into the separator chamber.

3A11. Vent pipe. The vent pipe is a ½-inch pipe extending from the hole in the middle of the separator floor to which it is connected, down through the center axis of the unit and out. The external end is open to the atmosphere.

3A12. Water level. The water level in the unit is maintained at about ½ inch above the topmost coil of the heat exchanger by means of two overflow pipes, diametrically opposite each other. Figure 2–2, being a schematic view, shows only one of the overflow pipes.

3A13. Overflow pipes. These two pipes, called *low overflow pipes,* carry the undistilled and concentrated brine down through the overflow heat exchanger. For safety purposes a second pair of *high* overflow pipes is placed between the regular short overflow pipes; they too drain into the overflow heat exchanger.

3A14. Vent damper. The *vent damper* is a device connected to the vent pipe of the unit in order to damp out wide and sudden fluctuations of air pressure. Such fluctuations occur on occasion in certain types of submarines when a torpedo is fired or during a quick dive, or under other conditions.

The distilling unit is sensitive to changes of air pressure because the surface of the boiling water is open to the atmosphere inside the submarine through the vent. With rapid changes of pressure, the unit will stop operating since the penetration of the air through the vent, reaching the space where the water is boiling, will cause a sudden increase of compressor pressure. This difficulty is overcome by installing the dampening device on the vent pipe. A functional diagram of this device is shown in Figure 3–2.

The vent damper is a Y-shaped piping arrangement connected into the vent. One upper branch of the Y is open to the air through a ¹⁄₁₆-inch hole in a diaphragm. The small size of this hole causes any wide and sudden changes in hull pressure to be communicated very gradually to the surface of the boiling water in the unit. A stop valve is placed at the end of this branch for a good supply of air at starting. This valve should be opened

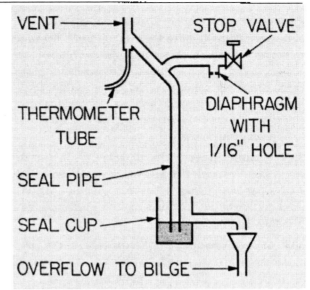

Figure 3–2.   *Vent damper.*

wide when starting the unit, and should be shut after the unit is operating.

The lower branch of the Y leads down into an open top seal cup which is about 4 inches in diameter and 5 inches high. This cup should be filled with water to the level of the overflow connection before starting the unit.

The action of the dampening device is as follows: If the air pressure in the hull decreases, there will be a small discharge of steam into the water in the seal cup with no other apparent changes. If the air pressure in the hull rises, the increased pressure on the water in the open seal cup will force some water up the seal pipe, to balance the difference in pressure between the unit and the hull. Air will gradually pass into the unit through the diaphragm ¹⁄₁₆-inch hole and equalize the pressure at such a rate that the unit will have time to adjust itself to the changed conditions without stopping.

The unit will operate normally during this adjustment period and the only difference noticeable will be an increase in pressure of the compressor. The pressure will gradually drop back to normal.

Any liquid running from the vent will pass out of the seal pipe and overflow into the funnel, as it would without the attachment, under all pressure conditions in the submarine.

B. THE TWO-LOBED ROOTS-CONNERSVILLE COMPRESSOR

3B1. Impellers. The vapor is compressed by the rotating action of the two double-lobed impellers, each a one-piece bronze casting, accurately machined. They are, in effect, a pair of two-tooth gears of involute form. The drive is by belt from a motor mounted above the compressor case to a pulley on the shaft of one impeller. Opposite to the drive end, a pair of one-to-one precision gears turns the other impeller. Reference to the circular inset view in Figure 2–1 shows this construction clearly. Figure 5–1 shows an exploded view of the two-lobed compressor.

3B2. Impeller gears. The impeller gears run in an oil bath contained in an oiltight housing. The shafts pass out through packing glands. An oil level indicator is provided on the gear housing. See also Section 5B1.

3B3. Impeller housing. The impellers are enclosed in their own housing which has semicircular ends (Figure 2–2). The vapor enters from the vapor separator, passes through channels to the top of the compressor, is carried around between the impellers and the casing, and is discharged as compressed vapor to the heat exchanger.

3B4. Impellers not lubricated. There is no contact either between the impellers or between the impellers and the impeller housing. There is a slight clearance of a few thousandths of an inch around all faces of the impellers. Therefore no lubrication is needed inside this housing.

3B5. Slip. Since there is higher pressure on the discharge side than on the inlet or suction side, there is a backward slippage of the vapor. This slippage is slight, and reduces the compression only by a very small amount.

3B6. Compressing action. As the impellers rotate in opposite directions, each in turn alternately cuts off a pocket of vapor when it reaches a vertical position, as is shown for the left impeller in Figure 2–2. When this impeller reaches the position where that pocket of vapor may escape, the impeller lobes, continuing to rotate, squeeze or compress the vapor. This type of compressor is very efficient. The fact that no oil is needed inside the compressor housing insures that no oil can get into the distilled water.

3B7. Compressor motor. A 7½-hp motor with necessary starting and protective electrical equipment is bolted on top of the compressor casing. The drive to the compressor shaft pulley is by four texrope V-belts.

3B8. Variable pitch drive. The drive pulley on the motor is of the adjustable or variable pitch type. The amount of variation of pitch is small, 5.400 to 6.600 inches' pitch diameter of the pulley, and is intended only to adjust the tension of the belts. The four left-hand sides of the pulley grooves are attached to a sliding sleeve. Rotating this sleeve moves the left-hand sides toward or away from the four stationary right-hand sides. Since the belt grooves are V-shaped in section, this motion increases or decreases the pitch diameter.

Adjusting the variable pitch drive. Loosen the setscrews on the sleeve. Turn the adjustable part of the pulley with the special spanner wrench found in the spare parts box until the belts are at proper tension. The proper tension is that which gives the belts, when running, a bow of about 1 inch on the slack side. Then tighten the setscrews.

3B9. Upper head plate. This heavy copper nickel plate is $1\frac{3}{16}$ inch thick. It is the main support of the distiller, and is fastened securely to brackets which are bolted to a bulkhead. To it is bolted the shell of the unit. In the bottom of the head plate, inside the shell, is fastened a casing of $\frac{3}{16}$-inch thick copper-nickel, forming a separate compartment $\frac{3}{4}$ inch high and of nearly the same diameter as the shell.

Four short $1\frac{3}{4}$-inch o. d. tubes are set into the head plate and direct the vapor from the separator to the compressor, without permitting it to enter the head plate compartment (see Figure 2–2). After the vapor is compressed, it is discharged from the compressor down through a 3-inch hole into the upper head plate compartment. The vapor leaves this head plate compartment, or discharge vapor space, at the sides through eight 1-inch o. d. pipes called upper headers, which lead down to the heat exchanger tubes.

NOTE. The Roots-Connersville two-lobe compressor has been replaced on most submarines by the General Motors three-lobe compressor. This compressor is described in Section 7B.

C. CONTROL DEVICES

3C1. Pressure gage. A 0- to 15-psi pressure gage (Figure 3–3) is connected into the discharge vapor space of the upper head plate, which, for operating control, provides continuous reading of the

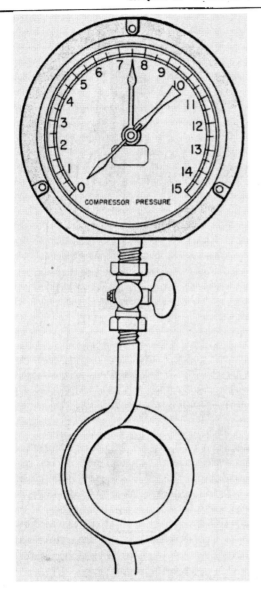

Figure 3-3.   Pressure gage.

ressure of the vapor going into the heat ex-
hanger.

C2. Vent thermometer. A distant reading dial
hermometer indicates the temperature in the vent
ipe. The bulb of the thermometer (Figure 3-4),
nserted in the vent pipe, is connected by a 9-foot
rmored capillary tubing to the dial which is grad-
ated from 30° F. to 240° F.

C3. Weir. The *weir* (Figure 3-5) measures the
ate of flow of the overflow brine discharge. The
verflow pipe leads out at the bottom of the unit,

then turns vertically upward along the side to such
a height that the interior overflow heat exchanger
is always full of liquid. The top of the pipe is
open, and also very near the top is an open vertical
slot 3 inches long and 1/16 inch wide. This slot is
the weir, through which the liquid flows. The
weir has a scale alongside it, and the height of
the liquid pouring through the weir indicates the
rate of flow in gallons per hour (gph), the maximum reading being 50 gph.

Just below the weir slot is a cup, 3¼ x 6 x 2
inches high, surrounding the weir pipe and silver

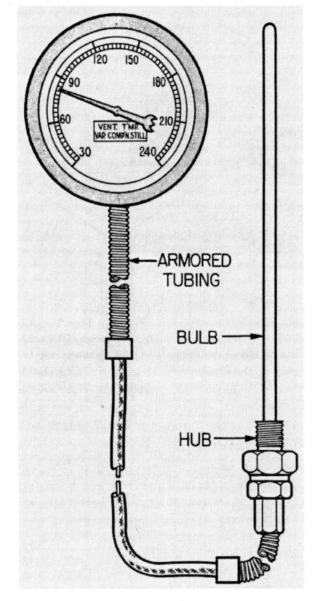

Figure 3-4.   Vent thermometer.

brazed to it, into which the liquid falls. From the bottom of the cup the brine flows through a drain pipe, to a temporary brine receiver tank, and finally to the sea.

Care of the weir. The weir slot must be kept clean and free of any deposit at all times, otherwise the readings will be in error.

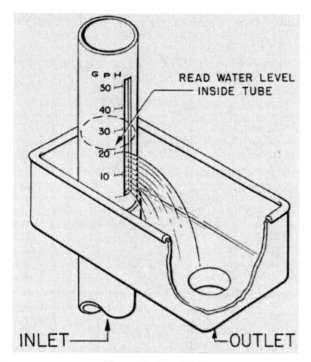

Figure 3-5. Weir.

Reading the weir. The liquid flows out of the slot and down into the cup in a curve. Care should be taken in reading the scale not to sight this outside curving part of the flow against the scale, or the reading will be too low. One should sight through the slot, reading the highest level of the liquid *inside* the weir against the scale. With sea water feed, there should always be a minimum of 20 gph flowing.

3C4. Relief valve. This valve (Figure 3–6) is located on the upper head plate adjacent to the compressor. It connects through the head plate into the compressor discharge space, to prevent overloading of the compressor motor. The valve is normally closed under spring pressure set at 7½ psi. It can also be manually opened at any time by lifting the lever. It is a safety valve, not a control valve.

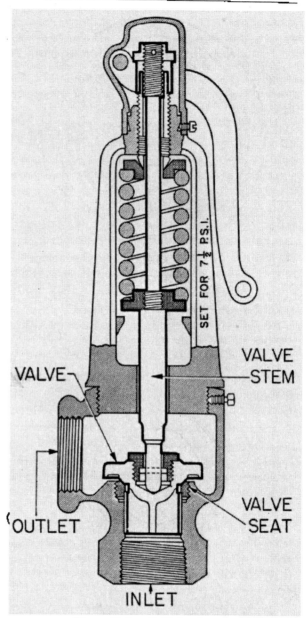

Figure 3-6. Relief valve.

3C5. Bypass valve. The bypass valve (Figure 3–7) is not a separate valve, nor connected into the system as ordinary valves are. It is, instead, an integral part of the upper head plate. The bypass valve opening connects the compressor discharge space and the vapor chamber above the boiling sea water (Figure 2–1). The round part at the bottom is a baffle and is open at both ends (Figure 3–7). The bypass valve is normally closed during distillation, but it is temporarily opened at starting, as described in Section 4B1.

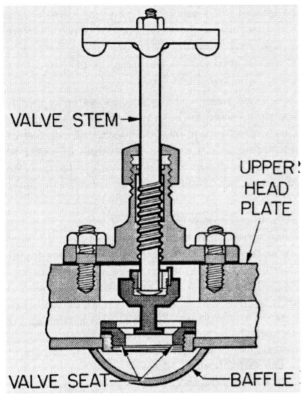

Figure 3-7.   Bypass valve.

The total resultant pressure of these opposing forces is the desired reduced pressure as set by the spring. The piston-and-stem arrangement further tends to damp out vibrations caused by pressure surges of the feed water.

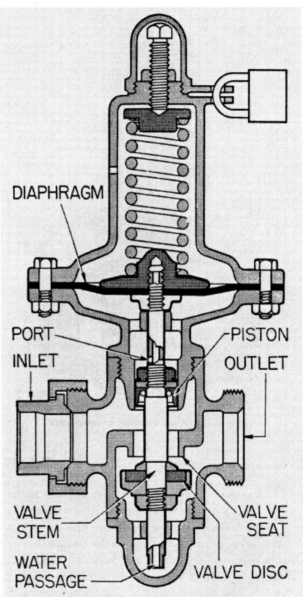

Figure 3-8.   Pressure reducing valve.

3C6. Pressure reducing valve. The pressure reducing valve (Figure 3–8) is connected into the sea water feed line between the feed pump and the feed water strainers. The incoming pressure through the pump may vary from 35 to 150 psi.

This reducing valve measures 9¾ inches in height. There are two separate airtight compartments in the valve, divided by a rubber diaphragm. In the upper compartment is a spring, which may be set to provide a given reduced pressure by means of the adjusting screw. The cover cap over the adjusting screw is secured by a padlock to prevent tampering.

The lower compartment is further divided into two separate spaces by a small piston attached to the middle of the stem, the piston sliding in a cylinder (Figure 3–8). The stem has a hole drilled through from its lower end to just above the piston, where a port leads out into the space above the piston. Figure 3–8 shows how the feed water bears both upward against the piston and downward against the valve disk, thus balancing. The water in the outlet side of the valve also flows up through the stem and bears against the diaphragm, keeping the spring in balance at its set pressure.

3C7. Flow control valve. A *flow control valve* (Figure 3–9) is installed in each feed line going to the two units. This valve, sometimes called a feed valve, is a conventional globe valve, installed just after the feed water strainers. A scale alongside the handle stem indicates the number of turns which have been given, and a dial on the

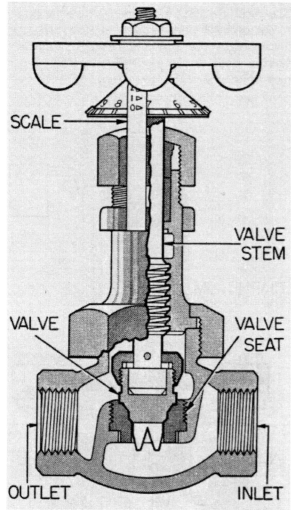

Figure 3-9.   Flow control or feed valve.

stem shows the amount of any one turn. Thus any position of the valve may be precisely read, and exactly repeated at a later time. The valve is so designed that equal openings give equal increases in the rate of flow.

3C8. Feed pump. The main sea water supply to the unit is fed in by a centrifugal type motor-driven feed pump, bulkhead mounted, capable of delivering 3 to 4 gallons per minute of water at 30 psi gage pressure. The feed may also be from auxiliary salt water supply, or from fresh water supply.

3C9. Water tanks. a. *Distilled water.* The distilled water, from both units, flows into a *distilled water receiver* or tank (Figure 2-3), made of nonferrous metal, of approximately 46 gallons capacity. Air at 10 psi is admitted at the top of the tank to give a head pressure. A petcock is provided for sampling. There is also a vent and a drain to the bilge. Piping connections lead to the desuperheater tank, to the battery water tanks, and to the ship's tanks.

b. *Brine receiver.* The overflow of concentrated brine flows from the weirs to a brine receiver or tank, made of copper nickel, of approximately 23 gallons capacity. Air at 30 psi is admitted at the top of the tank to provide a head when discharging overboard. There is a vent and a drain to the bilge. The drain to the bilge has a side-swing connection leading either overboard or to fresh water storage when feeding fresh water.

D. THE DESUPERHEATER

3D1. Desuperheater. An 8-gallon *desuperheater tank*, fed by a pipe from the distilled water tank (Figure 2-3), is supported above the units. A water level gage is attached to the desuperheater tank, and an overflow pipe leads to the bilge. From the bottom of the desuperheater tank, a ¼-inch tube leads to each of the compressors and into the impeller housings above the impellers. Valves in these tubes are adjusted to cause the distilled water to flow as drops, not as a steady stream on the impeller lobes. Since the drip is inside the compressors and hence not visible, a *sight feed glass* is inserted in each tube just outside the compressor with a glass window through which the water drops may be seen to pass. In

normal operation of the units the desuperheater flow is at a rate of 200 drops or more per minute. This is a very rapid flow and is the rate that exists just before the flow becomes a steady stream in the sight glass.

3D2. Need for desuperheater. When steam generated by boiling liquid at atmospheric pressure and a temperature of 212° F. is compressed mechanically to a pressure between 3 to 6 psi, the steam is superheated and reaches a temperature of 285° to 400° F. in the compressor. If this compression is carried on in the presence of water, the water removes the superheat from the steam and allows it to pass into the distiller at a temperature of saturated steam, which is 222° F. at 3 psi and

230° F. at 6 psi gage. Desuperheating is needed for two purposes:

a. Water from the desuperheater tank dripping on the impellers keeps the impellers and their shafts cooled. This cooling action prevents too great an expansion of the impellers by heat, thus retaining the required clearance of the impellers. It also prevents the shaft packing from getting too hot, which would cause rapid deterioration of the packing.

b. Better heat transfer is obtained from saturated steam than from superheated steam. A rapid rate of heat transfer is necessary to assist in keeping the feed water boiling; the quicker the steam condenses, the lower the pressure on the discharge side of the compressor will be.

Distilled water must be used for this desuperheating process. Ordinary fresh water contains various minerals and chemical compounds. These substances, while harmless to human beings, would be deposited on the impellers (since only the water vaporizes) and would gradually build up to a thickness that would cause the impellers to bind.

4

OPERATION OF THE
MODEL S DISTILLING UNIT

A. PRIMARY OPERATIONS

4A1. Checking the oil levels in the compressor. The proper oil for use in the distilling unit compressor is Navy Symbol 1150 or SAE 70 for the Roots-Connersville type and SAE 40 or Navy Symbol 9370 for the General Motors type. The oil levels in each compartment should be individually set after installation is completed. Pour approximately ⅔ of a quart of oil into the front oil compartment (pulley end) and mark the level on the sight glass. Pour approximately 1⅓ quarts of oil into the gear end (opposite end from pulley) and mark the level on the glass (the levels should stabilize about one-half full in the sight glasses). *Never use oil lighter than Navy Symbol 1150* in the Roots-Connersville compressor. The oil levels in the compressor are critical and should be kept as near as possible to the level indicated by the above procedure.

The oil level in the gage glasses will not read correctly during operation, due to the violent agitation in the oil compartments. The oil level should be checked at least once every 24 hours of continuous service by stopping the unit and noting the level after about a 20-minute rest. If the level is below the mark on the gage glass, add sufficient oil to raise the level and then start operating.

4A2. Checking the tightness of belts. Belts may be tightened by adjusting the variable pitch sheave attached to the motor. Loosen the belt adjustment screws in this sheave and turn the adjustable part of the pulley with a spanner wrench until the belts are at proper tension. Belts, while running, should bow out about an inch on the slack side from a straight line between the faces of the pulleys. If the belts are pulled up too tightly they may distort the compressor and cause the impellers to bind. Suitable wrenches will be found in the distilling unit spare parts box.

B. STARTING OPERATIONS

4B1. Starting

a. *Feed.* Start the feed pump and open the main supply valve on the feed line.

b. *Strainers.* Check the valves on the strainer manifold to be sure the flow is open through one strainer.

c. *Overflow.* Open the feed valve and allow the unit to fill to the proper level with water as evidenced by *flow* through the overflow cup. Adjust the feed valve to determine the normal operating setting. Note the setting and feed pressure for future use. Shut the feed valve. The flow to the unit during operation is approximately 60 gallons per hour and the flow control valve setting will depend on the pressure in the feed line. With a given pressure to the feed line, the condition of the strainers will also change the valve setting. To determine the normal operating setting of the flow

control valve, allow water to flow through the unit after filling and adjust the valve so that the flow through the weir will be exactly at 50 gph.

d. *Heaters.* Turn on the main switch (if provided), then snap on the 4 heater switches, one at a time. Observe the ammeter readings as each switch is turned on to insure that all heaters and switches are working properly.

CAUTION. Heaters are designed to operate only while they are submerged and will burn out unless covered with water. Do not turn the heaters on at any time unless the unit is full of water as evidenced by a flow through the weir.

e. *Bypass.* Open the bypass valve on top of the unit and turn the field rheostat counterclockwise all the way to the left (lowest speed).

f. *Motor.* About 30 minutes after starting the electric heaters start the vapor compressor motor.

CAUTION. Always start the motor at the lowest speed and with the bypass valve fully open.

g. *Desuperheater.* Start the desuperheater drip at about 200 drops per minute, after starting the compressor motor.

h. *Feed valve.* When a surge occurs in the overflow cup, start the feed pump and open the feed valve to one-third of the normal operating setting. As soon as the bypass is shut, open the feed valve immediately to the normal operating setting.

i. *Bypass.* Shut the bypass slowly when steam begins coming out of the vent pipe and the vent thermometer reading increases rapidly. Never allow the compressor discharge pressure to rise above 6.5 psi. With a clean unit, while distilling, the discharge pressure will be 3 to 4 psi with the bypass valve shut. At the time that the compressor is first started the water in the distilling unit is not at its boiling point. With no steam supplied, the compressor will take in air through the vent pipe and discharge it through the condensate pipe. Steam will gradually form and displace the air. In 60 to 90 minutes, the water in the unit will boil violently, supplying more than enough steam for the compressor. The first indication of this boiling will be a sudden flow in the weir, even over the top of the tube. A few seconds later the vent temperature will rise rapidly and steam will appear at the vent. The pressure gage will fall about a pound from the reading indicated before the unit started to distill. Now shut the bypass valve slowly, allowing 30 seconds to 1 minute to close it completely.

j. *Vent thermometer.* Check the temperature of the vent thermometer after about 3 minutes of operation, during which time steam will be escaping from the vent. The thermometer should read 212° F. The thermometer sometimes gets out of adjustment during shipment. It should read 212° F. when the vent first starts steaming. If necessary, the thermometer should be adjusted as follows: Unscrew the front cover; hold the spindle with a screwdriver; move the pointer with a finger so that the reading will be 212° F. when free; replace the cover.

k. *Heaters.* The temperature of the feed water and the amount of scale present will determine how many heaters must be used. After the initial surge through the overflow weir cup, the amount of overflow will drop off. Adjustment of the feed valve must be made to obtain a *minimum* overflow of 20 gph (indicated by the overflow level in the weir). All heater switches must normally be left *on* to maintain steady operation with this rate of overflow from a clean unit. A high rate of overflow will retard scaling of the heating surfaces. When an overflow rate of about 30 gph can be maintained, some of the heaters may be turned off.

l. *Adjustment of feed rate.* During the adjustment of the feed rate to the unit, the vent will stop steaming and the vent thermometer will drop below 212° F. When this takes place, reduce the feed rate about $\frac{1}{20}$ of a turn on the flow valve control.

CAUTION. Make all changes in the feed rate slowly. If the thermometer reading continues to drop, reduce the feed rate still further by slow adjustment of the feed valve at about 5-minute intervals until the thermometer reading remains steady. The rate of drop should not be over 3° to 5° F. per minute.

Control of the temperature of the vent thermometer is essential, otherwise the unit will take in too much air through the vent, build up a high pressure on the compression side, and shut down. During the adjusting operation, the pressure on the compressor gage may go up $\frac{3}{4}$ of a pound above normal. If this happens, additional heater switches should be turned on until normal pressure returns and steam issues at the vent. The additional heaters may then be turned off and adjustments of feed rate continued. A flow through the weir must always be maintained and if it slackens below the required amount, the flow rate should be gradually increased.

CAUTION. The weir tube reading is affected for 3 to 5 minutes by *any change.* Always wait for at least 3 minutes after any change before reading the weir tube.

m. *Desirable feed rate.* A feed rate corresponding to an overflow of 30 gallons per hour with a slight trace of steam coming from the vent pipe, and a vent temperature reading 200° to 212° F. may be considered good operation. The adjustment period usually requires about 30 minutes.

C. OPERATIONS WHILE RUNNING

4C1. Means of controlling. Control of the distillation process during operation is effected chiefly by means of the *vent thermometer* and the *weir*. The weir reading indicates directly the rate of overflow and indirectly the feed rate, the latter being the factor which is to be controlled. After the distiller is in full operation, attention need be given only to these two controls and the pressure gage.

4C2. Operation of the vent thermometer. The unit is usually quite stable with a constant vent temperature between 200° F. and 212° F. The vent temperature should be read at least every 30 minutes. If it has fallen below 200° F. the feed rate should be cut very slightly; if it is up to 212° F. and steaming excessively at the vent, the feed rate should be increased slightly. The distilled water drip for desuperheating in the compressor should be checked from time to time to maintain about 200 drops per minute.

A falling reading on the vent thermometer shows that the unit is losing heat. If this is accompanied by a pulsation on the ammeter of several amperes, and the discharge pressure gage fluctuates more than ½ pound, the unit is taking air through the vent pipe. To remedy this condition turn on an additional heater switch, reduce the feed rate slightly, then turn off the extra heater switch. Repeat this remedy if necessary.

After the unit has been run continuously for a period of 4 or 5 hours without any change in power or feed conditions, a slight amount of excess heat may be available as indicated by the appearance of steam discharging at the vent, and the vent thermometer rising to approximately 212° F. It is advisable to compensate for this excessive heat by gradually increasing the feed rate until only a slight feather of steam remains at the vent and the vent thermometer falls a little below 212° F.

Should the unit lose too much heat, the vent temperature will fall considerably below 212° F. and air will be taken in through the vent. Under this condition the compressor discharge pressure will rise rapidly due to overload, and the relief valve on the head plate of the unit will blow steam. If this happens, the bypass valve should be immediately opened wide and the unit treated as if it were being started.

When the operators are familiar with the behavior of the indicating instruments, they should anticipate changes in the heat balance and make corrections accordingly. The unit will operate over several hours after adjustments without need of changing the rate of feed or cutting the heater switches in or out if the power conditions remain reasonably constant.

D. OPERATION OF THE MOTOR

4D1. Operating the motor. The feed pressure and motor speed should remain substantially constant to obtain the best operation. If the line voltage varies, the speed of the compressor and the corresponding output of the distilling unit may be somewhat increased or decreased by turning the field rheostat to change the speed of the motor.

Operation of the controller is obtained by pressing the start button. The motor is started through two steps of starting resistors, and acceleration is controlled by the action of series relays. The relays are adjusted to close the accelerating contactors on successive current inrushes and at 30 amperes' decreasing current. An electrical interlock on the final accelerating contactor opens the coil circuit to the first accelerating contactor which remains open during the running period.

Low voltage protection is provided and, in the event of voltage failure, the equipment can be restarted when the voltage has been restored to the line by pressing the start button. Stopping of the motor is effected by pressing the stop button.

The operation of the controller is subject at all times to the operation of the overload relay, which opens the circuit to the main line contactor on excessive overloads. After the overload relay has tripped, it will reset automatically, but it is necessary to press the start button to restart the motor.

Speed adjustment above or below normal is obtained by inserting a rheostat in the shunt field circuit and varying the resistance.

The operation of the motor should be continuously observed during the first few hours of operation, noting the condition of the bearings, commutator, and other parts, and observing the temperature and balance of the motor.

The heat balance of the distilling system is sensitive and all changes in the operating conditions should be made slowly.

E. STOPPING OPERATIONS

4E1. Stopping.

a. *Heaters.* Cut off all heaters.

b. *Motor.* Stop the motor.

c. *Bypass.* Open the bypass valve.

d. *Desuperheater.* Shut off the desuperheater drip.

e. *Feed.* Continue feeding for 1½ to 2 hours. This continued feed is for flushing the tubes. The flow during this flushing should be through the full slot in the weir. After flushing, close the feed valve and secure the feed pump.

f. *Desuperheater tank.* Fill the desuperheater supply tank with distilled water before discharging the condensate receivers.

4E2. Retarding scale formation. Scale will gradually accumulate on the heating surfaces during normal operation. When the unit is shut down from time to time, it must be left filled with sea water, as the cold sea water exerts a solvent action on the scale.

F. HULL PRESSURE CHANGES

4F1. Variation of hull pressure. Under ordinary conditions the unit may be operated equally as well under the water as on the surface. When running submerged on the ship's main motors, the load variation will influence the line voltage, and the motor speed should be adjusted as well as possible with the field rheostat to maintain a constant output of distilled water.

Increase in the hull pressure will increase the pressure readings on the compressor gage and raise the boiling point of the sea water in the distilling unit. Additional electric heaters should be turned on to compensate for the additional heat required when the hull pressure increases. A reduction in the air pressure within the hull will tend to make the distilling unit discharge steam at the vent.

A rapid rise in pressure within the hull will make it impossible to increase the heat sufficiently to maintain operations. The unit will take in air at the vent and cease to operate. When this difficulty occurs, the bypass valve should be opened immediately and the unit treated as in starting operations.

Changes in hull pressure will occur for a variety of reasons. Such changes may occur after venting the negative tank; after firing a torpedo; when running on the engines on the surface; and on opening and closing the air lock doors. (For effect of snorkel operations, see Section 8A5.) To help alleviate these conditions, a water seal or damper is attached to the vent. The construction and operation of this vent damper are described in Section 3A14.

G. OPERATING WITH FRESH WATER

4G1. Distilling fresh water. To distill fresh water taken aboard from an outside source, or sea water distilled only once, the following variation in operation should be followed:

a. *Vapor pressure.* The compressor pressure will be about ½ pound lower, that is, about 2½ to 3½ psi with a clean unit. The reason for this is that the feed water is fresh, and therefore its normal condensation point does not need to be raised.

The heat put into the vapor by compression in this case is used to balance the heat loss through the insulation, the condensate, and the brine overflow. See Section 2A2.

b. *Overflow.* The rate of overflow may be reduced from one-quarter to one-half that required for sea water distillation.

c. *Heaters.* Under these conditions, after the bypass valve is shut, fewer heaters may be used.

5

CARE AND MAINTENANCE
OF THE MODEL S DISTILLING UNIT

A. RETARDING SCALE FORMATION

5A1. Scale formation. The coils of the distilling unit gradually become coated with scale, and if the operation is continued over too long a period the accumulation of scale will tend to make the tube cones stick together, and difficult to separate. Since the tubes are made of comparatively soft copper nickel, separating them cannot be accomplished without the certain danger of damaging the cones.

5A2. Flushing during operation to retard scale. After every 10 to 20 hours of continuous operation all heaters should be turned on and the unit operated about 3 hours with maximum feed allowing stable operation. If the compressor discharge pressure continues to increase and does not come down after flushing, more heaters should be used and the overflow rate increased for the remainder of the patrol or until such time as the flushing will reduce the compressor discharge pressure.

Operators should endeavor to keep the compressor discharge pressure as low as possible. When the pressure begins to increase and fails to return to the initial operating pressure after flushing, the overflow rate during operation should be gradually increased by using more heaters and increasing the feed rate. The unit should not be operated for more than 22 continuous hours between flushings.

The periodic flushings will retard the increase in operating pressure, but this will nevertheless gradually rise. A rise in pressure of approximately 2¼ pounds from the initial operating pressure of 3½ pounds may be considered safe. That is, 5¾ pounds is the upper limit of compressor gage pressure, at a compressor speed of 1100 rpm. In an emergency, 6¼ pounds may be used as the upper gage pressure limit.

If the discharge pressure is allowed to increase much beyond the pressures indicated, cleaning by the acid method will be extremely difficult and the type of scale formation will make it necessary to disassemble and clean mechanically, which is always difficult.

Every effort should be made to return to the base or tender with distilling units operating at 5¾ pounds or less compressor discharge pressure. Under these conditions the stills may be easily and quickly cleaned by chemical methods without disassembly.

5A3. Flushing during shutdown period. The rate of scaling will be retarded if the distilling unit is operated at all times with a *minimum* of 20 gallons per hour overflow, and, after the unit is secured, flushed for a period of 1½ to 2 hours with cold sea water at a rate of approximately 60 gallons per hour overflow, with the weir left filled with sea water. Under the above conditions the distilling unit should operate for a period of 350 to 400 hours.

B. THE TWO-LOBED ROOTS-CONNERSVILLE COMPRESSOR

5B1. Lubrication. The compressor is lubricated from two reservoirs, one at each end. Each oil reservoir is supplied with an oil level indicator which has previously had the proper oil level marked on the gage. The oil level should be checked every 24 hours and oil added as needed when the compressor is not running.

Two vertical ½-inch nipples with couplings closed with two ½-inch pipe plugs are provided for filling the oil compartment. The pipe plugs are removed and oil poured into the couplings until the proper level is reached. The oil may be drained from the compartment by opening the ½-inch petcocks. Oil is retained in the oil compartment by oil seal rings or packing glands.

The reservoir of oil at the pulley end of the compressor lubricates the ball bearings by a slinger ring attached to the drive shaft. The reservoir of oil at the opposite end from the pulley lubricates the timing gears and ball bearings at that end of the compressor by the splashing of the gears. All the bearings and gears run at a high temperature, and no oil lighter than Navy Symbol 1150 (SAE 70) should be used in the Roots-Connersville compressor.

On the old type vapor compressors, steam seals were used and leakage was carried away through a drain pipe into the vapor separator and out through the vent pipe. These seals were a source of trouble and on the later type compressor they have been replaced by packing glands. Steam leakage is now prevented by the use of stuffing box glands. These glands should be adjusted so that they will be just tight enough to prevent leakage. Excessive tightness will damage the packing and shaft sleeves, causing excessive heating and the impellers will stick. The gland nuts must be tightened evenly. When steam leakage cannot be stopped by tightening the glands, new packing must be installed. This may be done without dismantling the compressor. The nuts are loosened first and then the gland is backed out.

Each gland is packed thus: one ring of Johns-Manville No. 360, three rings of Johns-Manville No. 610, one ring of Johns-Manville No. 360.

Remove the first ring of No. 360 packing, using the packing hook found in the spare parts box, and one ring of No. 610. Insert two new rings of No. 610 and one ring of No. 360. Insert the gland and tighten carefully. This should make the stuffing box tight. However, if this is not satisfactory, remove all five rings from the stuffing box and insert one ring of No. 360, three rings of No. 610 and one ring of No. 360. Tighten gradually and evenly as recommended. The packing gland which is split may be removed from the shaft during the packing operation if found necessary.

When a complete overhaul of the compressor is necessary it must be removed from the distilling unit.

5B2. Keeping oil out of the compressor. Should oil for any reason get into the steam compressor it will be left inside the $\frac{1}{4}$-inch tubes of the heat exchanger coils, causing the pressure to go up and the heat transfer rate to fall off, besides contaminating the distillate with oil. A thin film of oil may be noticed on the surface of the condensate. To remove oil from the tubes, shut the unit down and flush with feed water until the overflow feed runs cool. Shut off the feed. Disconnect the condensate piping and make a connection to the condensate header with hose or piping, running the open end to just below the compressor. Add about two or three gallons of any pure oil solvent such as naphtha, to this open end, completely filling the tube bundle. Drain and repeat with the same solvent. Reconnect the unit and continue operation.

5B3. Removing compressor from the unit. In removing the compressor, proceed as follows:

a. Remove the belt guard, loosen the variable pitch drive, and take off the belts.

b. Disconnect the motor leads and take out the bolts holding the motor support on top of the compressor.

c. Remove the compressor lagging and after draining the oil from the compressor take off all the oil piping.

d. Remove the pressure gage and piping where needed.

e. It is advisable to mark the oil piping so that it may be put back in the exact location.

f. Take off all the nuts and lock washers attaching the compressor to the distilling unit, breaking the gasketed joint by using jack bolts if available and lift off the compressor.

NOTE. It is very desirable that any repairs to a vapor compressor be done by a tender.

5B4. Disassembling compressor (new type). Figure 5–1 shows an exploded view of the two-lobed compressor. Remove the motor-supporting base. Remove the drive and cover, and then remove the gear house cover. Mark each gear hub and each shaft to be certain that the assembly of the timing gears will be exactly in the same position as before. Also mark a gear tooth and its mating groove to insure proper location of the impellers and gears.

Remove the taper pin on the timing gear which is pinned, using the taper pin punch in the compressor spare parts box.

CAUTION. Care should be exercised to avoid bending the shaft, by placing a heavy iron against the hub of the gear when driving out the pin.

Remove the gears by means of the gear puller provided in the compressor spare parts box. Remove the cap screws, and insert the $\frac{1}{4}$-inch cap screws provided in the spare parts box into the bearing carrier. With the aid of these screws, take out the bearing carrier. The carrier will contain the bearings and oil slingers.

On the drive end of the compressor the bearing lock nuts and then the cap screws must be removed. Remove the oil slinger. By means of the ¼-inch cap screws the bearing carriers may be pulled out. Remove the shims carefully.

Drive out the taper pins that locate the gear-end head plate and remove all cap screws and lock washers. By means of wedges, force the head plate from the cylinder. The drive-end head plate need not be removed.

Remove the glands from the shafts and take out all the packing.

Pull the impellers and shafts from the drive-end head plate.

Should it be necessary to replace the impellers or gears in the compressor, a complete new assembly must be used because gears and impellers are matched and cannot be used interchangeably. A complete set is provided in the spare parts box.

5B5. Assembling the compressor. Push the shafts with the impellers through the drive-end head plates and then place the gear-end head plate over the shafts and against the cylinders. Insert the taper pins to locate the head plate correctly in the original position. Insert the cap screws and draw them up uniformly tight. Do not insert and tighten one cap screw without installing and tightening the other simultaneously.

Insert the bearing carriers with the oil slingers and drive on the oil slingers using the drive tube provided in the compressor spare parts box.

Drive the bearings on the shafts and into the carriers against the oil slingers. On the gear end, follow with the spacer collar.

Heat the drive shaft gear in an oil bath to a temperature of about 250° F. and quickly place it over the shaft and press in the key. Set the impeller shaft in the correct timing position, using the gear spanner wrench from the spare parts box to turn the gear. Heat the driven shaft gear to about 250° F. in an oil bath, then quickly place it on the shaft and press in the taper pin. Check to be sure that the taper pin is in the proper location and will enter 80 percent of the distance by hand and then drive it in firmly, placing a heavy iron against the gear hub to prevent the bending of the shaft while driving the pin.

On the drive end, after installing the carriers, oil slingers, and bearings on both of the shafts, and placing the collar and slinger plate on the short shaft, tighten the lock nuts. By the use of laminated shims the axial position of the impellers must be adjusted to divide the total end clearance of .012 inches as nearly equally as possible between each end of the impeller and its head plate. The laminated shims are .002 inches thick. Any extra clearance should be left at the gear end when it is not possible to set the impellers exactly in the central position.

The clearance on the driving face of the lobe of the impeller on the drive shaft should be .016 inch and on the back of the lobe .006 inch. If the impellers strike after being set for these clearances, look for burrs, roughness, or particles of metal imbedded in the impeller.

If the impellers are not timed correctly with the taper pin driven firmly into the driven shaft, loosen the thrust bearing clamping plate and drive out the taper pin. Place a thin strip of metal of the proper thickness between the close impeller lobes and, by use of the gear spanner wrench (from the compressor spare parts box) placed on the gears, turn the impellers in the proper direction to cause the gear on the driven shaft to turn to the correct location. The gear fit is too tight on the shaft to permit movement with the spanner wrench. Put pressure on the gear with the spanner wrench and strike the hub of the gear, causing it to jump to a new position. The taper-pin hole in the gear shaft may be reamed and the taper pin driven in a little deeper. Tighten the thrust bearing clamping plate.

The impellers when correctly turned and located may be revolved easily by hand or spanner wrench.

The proper impeller clearances are:

Between tip and case top____ 0.004 in. to 0.006 in.
Between tip and case bottom_ 0.004 in. to 0.006 in.
End clearance (gear end)___ 0.004 in. to 0.006 in.
End clearance (drive end)__ 0.004 in. to 0.008 in.
Total end-clearance_____   0.012 in.
Tips and back of case_____ 0.004 in. to 0.006 in.
Open or front contour   0.008 in. to 0.010 in.
  clearance.
Closed or back contour   0.005 in. to 0.006 in.
  clearance.
Total impeller contour_____   0.016 in.

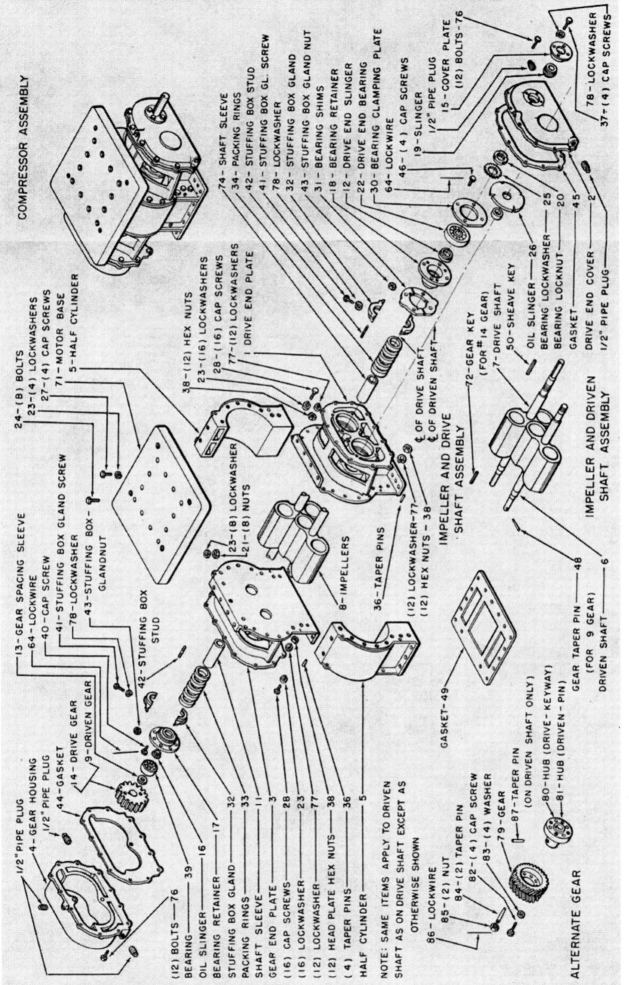

COMPRESSOR ASSEMBLY

74 — SHAFT SLEEVE
34 — PACKING RINGS
42 — STUFFING BOX STUD
41 — STUFFING BOX GL. SCREW
78 — LOCKWASHER
32 — STUFFING BOX GLAND
43 — STUFFING BOX GLAND NUT
31 — BEARING SHIMS
18 — BEARING RETAINER
12 — DRIVE END SLINGER
22 — DRIVE END BEARING
30 — BEARING CLAMPING PLATE
64 — LOCKWIRE
46 — (4) CAP SCREWS
19 — SLINGER
1/2" PIPE PLUG
15 — COVER PLATE
37 — (4) CAP SCREWS
78 — LOCKWASHER
(12) BOLTS — 76

24 — (8) BOLTS
23 — (4) LOCKWASHERS
27 — (4) CAP SCREWS
71 — MOTOR BASE
5 — HALF CYLINDER

38 — (12) HEX NUTS
23 — (16) LOCKWASHERS
28 — (16) CAP SCREWS
77 — (12) LOCKWASHERS
1 DRIVE END PLATE

¢ OF DRIVE SHAFT
¢ OF DRIVEN SHAFT

72 — GEAR KEY
(FOR #14 GEAR)

OIL SLINGER — 26
50 — SHEAVE KEY
7 — DRIVE SHAFT
BEARING LOCKWASHER — 25
BEARING LOCKNUT — 20
GASKET — 45
DRIVE END COVER — 2
1/2" PIPE PLUG

IMPELLER AND DRIVE
SHAFT ASSEMBLY

8 — IMPELLERS
36 — TAPER PINS
(12) LOCKWASHER — 77
(12) HEX NUTS — 38

23 — (8) LOCKWASHER
21 — (8) NUTS

42 — STUFFING BOX
STUD

GEAR TAPER PIN
(FOR 9 GEAR) — 48
DRIVEN SHAFT — 6

IMPELLER AND DRIVEN
SHAFT ASSEMBLY

1/2" PIPE PLUG
4 — GEAR HOUSING
1/2" PIPE PLUG
44 — GASKET
14 — DRIVE GEAR
9 — DRIVEN GEAR

13 — GEAR SPACING SLEEVE
64 — LOCKWIRE
40 — CAP SCREW
41 — STUFFING BOX GLAND SCREW
78 — LOCKWASHER
43 — STUFFING BOX — GLANDNUT

(12) BOLTS — 76
BEARING — 39
OIL SLINGER — 16
BEARING RETAINER — 17
STUFFING BOX GLAND — 32
PACKING RINGS — 33
SHAFT SLEEVE — 11
GEAR END PLATE — 3
(16) CAP SCREWS — 28
(16) LOCKWASHER — 23
(12) LOCKWASHER — 77
(12) HEAD PLATE HEX NUTS — 38
(4) TAPER PINS — 36
HALF CYLINDER — 5

NOTE: SAME ITEMS APPLY TO DRIVEN
SHAFT AS ON DRIVE SHAFT EXCEPT AS
OTHERWISE SHOWN

GASKET — 49
80 — HUB (DRIVE — KEYWAY)
81 — HUB (DRIVEN — PIN)
87 — TAPER PIN
(ON DRIVEN SHAFT ONLY)
79 — GEAR
83 — (4) WASHER
82 — (4) CAP SCREW
84 — (2) NUT
85 — (2) TAPER PIN
86 — LOCKWIRE

ALTERNATE GEAR

Figure 5-1.   Vapor compressor, two lobe (exploded view).

CAUTION. Do not drive against the shaft or any part mounted on the shaft after the thrust bearing has been clamped in place by the clamping plate.

Place safety wiring on the clamping plate cap screws. Reinstall the gear housing and drive-end housing, together with the drive shaft end cover and oil slinger.

Repack all packing glands with the proper packing, install the packing glands, and tighten them carefully.

Shellac the joint surfaces on the compressor and motor-supporting plate, and then insert and tighten the bolts uniformly.

C. CLEANING THE MODEL S DISTILLING UNIT

5C1. Methods of cleaning. The distilling surfaces of the unit are cleaned by either of two methods: (a) by using a muriatic acid (HCL) solution; or (b) by scraping and wire brushing.

The approved method of cleaning is the acid method. The acid method should be used only at a base or alongside a tender, as it requires special apparatus and an experienced crew. However, in case the acid method is not available, or if the unit is allowed to get too dirty for the acid method to be effective, the unit must be disassembled and cleaned mechanically.

5C2. Routine for acid cleaning. The Model S distilling unit may normally be cleaned by circulating a solution of 6.8 percent by weight of muriatic acid (HCL) in water through the still.

A 6.8 percent by weight muriatic acid solution is made up by adding 2 gallons of concentrated commercial muriatic acid (20° Baumé) to 10 gallons of fresh water.

A charge of 30 gallons of the 6.8 percent muriatic acid solution is required for each still. It should be circulated at a rate of about 60 gallons per hour through the still.

The following is a list of the equipment needed for acid cleaning both stills:

1 battery jar—about 45-gallon capacity
1 rubber container—about 5-gallon capacity
1 rubber measuring bucket
2 40- to 50-foot lengths of hose
4 4-foot lengths of hose
2 6-foot lengths of hose
2 6-inch lengths of hose
1 10-foot length of hose
1 12-foot length of hose
2 acid pumps

Miscellaneous brass pipe, fittings and valves, several Stillson and monkey wrenches, hose clamps, screwdriver, and pliers. Fresh water connection to deck of ship or dock.

12 gallons of HCL (20° Baumé)
Proceed as follows:

a. Drain the unit and disconnect all piping at the base comprising the feed, condensate, vent and overflow.

b. Connect a short length of pipe and a valve to each feed connection (valves 3 and 4, Figure 5–2).

c. Connect the two feed connections together into a **T**, using two 4-foot lengths of hose (1 and 2).

d. Connect two 4-foot long hoses (3 and 4) to the overflow connection and place the open ends in the 5-gallon rubber container.

e. Connect acid pump 2 as shown using the two 6-foot lengths of hose (5 and 7) and the 6-inch piece of hose (6) and a **T** with valve 2.

f. Run the two 40- or 50-foot lengths of hose (8 and 9) to the topside as shown.

g. Connect acid pump 1 using the two lengths of hose, 10 feet and 12 feet (11 and 12), and the 6-inch length (10) connected to a **T** and valve 1 as shown.

h. Measure 30 gallons of fresh water into the battery jar and mark the level.

i. Shut valves 3 and 4, open valve 1, prime acid pump 1 with fresh water and start pump 1.

j. Open valves 3 and 4 until the water runs from the overflow hose and nearly fills the 5-gallon rubber container.

NOTE. A man on topside should keep the water up to the mark in the battery jar as the units are being filled. Each unit holds approximately 16 gallons when full to the operating level.

k. Shut valves 3 and 4.

l. Prime acid pump 2 and start with valve 2 open.

m. Open valves 3 and 4.

n. Adjust valve 2 so that the level in the 5-gallon container is about constant. If pump 1 does not

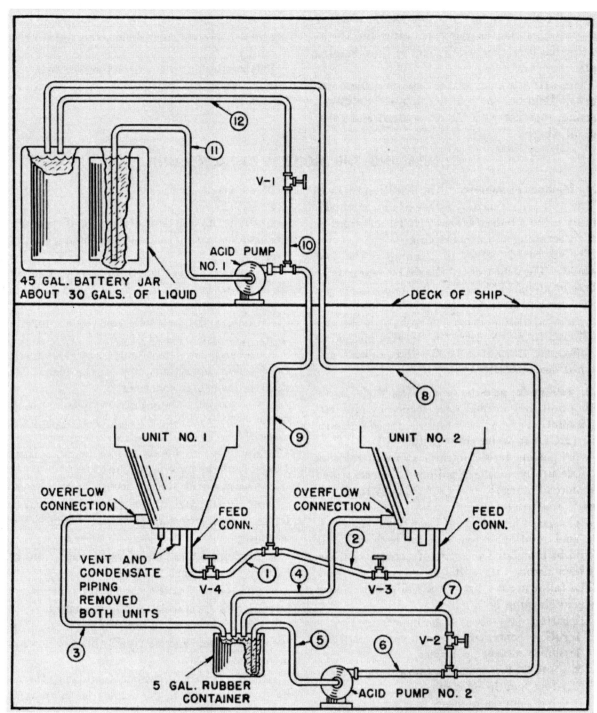

Figure 5-2. Acid cleaning piping arrangement.

give sufficient water through the units with valve 1 wide open it may be partially closed.

CAUTION. Do not shut valves 3 and 4 until valve 1 has been opened. The open end of hose 1 must not be below the level of the liquids in the battery jar.

o. When water has been circulating freely abc 15 minutes and all valves are adjusted, slowly a 12 gallons of 20° Baume muriatic acid to 1 battery jar. After all the acid has been add circulate the acid solution through the units : 2 hours.

p. At the end of 2 hours of acid circulation, place hose 8 overboard. When the level in the battery jar is near bottom, fill the jar with fresh water and keep it filled.

q. Circulate fresh water through the unit for an hour. Secure the pumps, disconnect the hoses, and drain the unit.

r. After every sixth acid cleaning, the shells of the unit should be removed and the coils inspected for scale. Until experience indicates otherwise, the outer two or three coils should be removed and inspected occasionally.

s. Reassemble the unit and fill with sea water.

NOTE. As the periodic inspections indicate, the units should be completely disassembled and the acid cleaning followed by a mechanical cleaning.

5C3. Routine for mechanical cleaning. When cleaning the Model S distilling unit by scraping and wire brushing, it is necessary to disassemble the unit. Use the following routine, taking particular care in handling the coils.

CAUTION. When disassembling the coils do not lay the coils on their sides. Stack the coils on a form, with the large ends down so as to prevent the union ends from touching the floor or deck.

5C4. Disassembling the Model S distilling unit. The disassembly procedure is as follows:

a. *Drain.* Drain unit completely of water.

b. *Braces.* Remove the braces at the bottom of the unit.

c. *Connections.* Remove the thermometer bulb and disconnect and remove all piping, comprising the feed, condensate, vent and overflow pipe with overflow cup.

d. *Insulation.* Remove the insulation from the shell and keep it in a dry place.

e. *Heaters.* Disconnect the electric heater plugs (heater plugs are the locking type and must be turned about a quarter turn before disconnecting). It is not recommended that the heaters be removed at this time.

f. *Glands.* Remove the packing glands on the vent and condensate pipes.

g. *Flanges.* Remove the small flange from the bottom of the lower shell section, using the jack bolts to break the gasketed joint. Take the two large nuts from the middle flange section and put over the shorter studs on opposite sides of the

bottom flange; replace the two small flange nuts and tighten to hold the cone sections together.

h. *Lower shell.* Remove all nuts from the middle flange of the shell and break the gasketed joint with the jack bolts provided. Take off the lower part of the shell.

i. *Upper shell.* Remove the nuts from the top flange and remove the upper half of the shell.

j. *Conical shells.* Remove the heaters and separate the two conical shells which make up the overflow heat exchanger.

5C5. Cleaning the surfaces a. *Shells.* Clean the surfaces of both shells and inner cone by wire brushing and scraping with soft copper scrapers and wire brushes.

b. *Coils.* Insert the pins (found in the spare parts box) into the clips, on each side at the top of the vapor separator to support it, and to remove its weight from the coils.

Clean as much of the outer surface of the lower coil as possible with the coil in place. Surfaces of coils must be kept wet, otherwise the scale will be hard to remove and the coils may not come apart without damage. Disconnect the eight unions at the top of the lower coil and one union at the bottom. Remove the coil and its three spacing cones, tapping with a wooden mallet if necessary. (A union wrench and wooden mallet will be found in the spare parts box.)

CAUTION. Great care must be taken not to let the coils drop. Handle them carefully so that the ends of the coils will not be damaged. A stand should be available for holding the coils. If none is available they may be placed in the lower shell for protection.

Clean the inner surface and complete the cleaning of the outer surface.

Clean each succeeding coil in the same way.

c. *Vapor separator.* Remove the pins from the vapor separator and wire brush the eight upper headers and the inner cylinder of the vapor separator.

CAUTION. Never attempt to remove more than one coil at a time from the distilling unit. If a coil sticks, light tapping around the top third of the coil with a wooden mallet will eventually loosen it. Do not hit the coil too hard as this may deform the copper nickel tubes or shape of the coil.

5C6. Assembling and testing the Model 5 distilling unit. Proceed as follows:

a. *Vapor separator.* Place the vapor separator in place and insert the pins to hold it.

b. *First operation in replacing coils.* Place back into position the last coil removed.

NOTE. A small arrow stamped on the tab of all coils aligns with the arrow stamped on the upper head plate, below the pulley.

c. *Upper and lower headers.* Connect all the unions of this coil to the upper headers. Connect the lower discharge header to the small coil header, positioning the discharge header as nearly vertical as possible.

d. *Routine for replacing coils.* Plug up the open unions on the lower discharge header. Connect a rubber hose to the outlet of the discharge header and fill the tubes with fresh water until water runs out of the open top unions. Inspect the bottom union and small coil header for leaks. If any union leaks, it may be corrected by lapping its two contacting faces with the opposing parts of a spare union; or by applying a film of white lead on the union. In this operation it is possible to check only the lower connections for leaks.

Remove the hose and top plug in the lower header so that the next coil can be set in place.

Place the three spacer cones inside the next coil and stand the small end of the coil in the steel coil assembly cone which should be placed directly below the unit.

Align the arrow on the coil in the assembly cone with the arrow on the top flange, raising the coil into position. Two men should lift the coil and assembly cone, keeping the part unions on the upper headers from striking the part unions on the coils as the coil is raised. A third man should guide the lower end of the coil and assembly as it is raised and place a small hydraulic or screw jack under the assembly cone, using a small piece of wood between the bottom of the assembly cone and the top of the jack. Raise the coil with the jack until the union on the small coil header aligns with the union on the discharge header. The coil must be jacked up so that the bottom union makes up exactly. The union should be started by hand, making sure that the threads are not crossed. Guide the coil so that the top unions do not strike the headers.

NOTE. If no jacking cone is available, pressure may be applied to the thick circular bottom header portion of the coil (⅜-inch diameter) using wood to cushion the force of the jack.

CAUTION. Great care must be taken not to put any pressure on the ¼-inch tube that leads from the ⅜-inch header at the bottom of the coils. In most of the union nut wrenches a small slot has been cut in the end. If absolutely necessary, fit this slot over the back part of the union and align the two parts of the unions before starting the union nut by hand.

After the bottom union is tightened firmly, the jack should be lowered. With no tension on the bottom of coil it is now possible to rotate the large (top) end of the coil so that the top unions will make up. The coil should now be jacked up a second time so that the top unions make up squarely with no bending of the tubes. Tighten the top unions and remove the jack.

e. *Replacing remaining coils.* Repeat the operations described in Section 5C6 on each of the remaining coils and spacer cones in sequence.

f. *Pins.* Remove the pins from the top of the vapor separator and allow the outer section of the separator to rest in the first coil.

g. *Testing the coil assembly.* Test the coil assembly for tightness by connecting a rubber tube to the outlet of the lower discharge header and filling the entire bundle with distilled water (about 2 gallons). Elevate the open end of the rubber tube above the upper unions on the coils so that the tube assembly may be filled completely with water. Leaks in the upper unions can be found and corrected without removing the coils. Leaks in lower unions will be indicated by water dripping but this cannot be corrected without removing the coils. For this reason, the lower unions and the ¼-inch tubes, to which the lower unions are attached and brazed to the ⅜-inch bottom header rings, should be tested as installed.

h. *Gaskets.* Use new flange gaskets where needed. Extra gaskets are provided in the spare parts box.

i. *Upper shell.* Place the upper half of the shell in position, matching the arrows on the flanges Screw all nuts halfway onto the studs.

j. *Lower shell.* Place the lower cones in position with the proper gaskets and install the heaters

Align with the arrows on the flanges and raise the conical shells into position. Install the middle flange nuts and tighten by hand.

k. *Packing gland.* Renew the packing in the condensate manifold packing gland, using a piece of ¾-inch pipe instead of condensate pipe. Screw the packing down hard and then back off on the packing gland nut; leave the nut installed loosely in the plate.

l. *Pipes.* Center the vent and condensate pipes in their respective holes in the bottom cover plate. Place the cover plate and supporting ring for the lagging over the studs and secure with the proper nuts, tightening firmly.

m. *Shell flanges.* Tighten the nuts on the upper and middle shell flanges.

n. *Packing.* Install packing in the vent pipe packing gland and tighten both the vent pipe and condensate pipe packing glands.

CAUTION. The nut on the vent pipe has a dual purpose: it acts as a packing gland nut, and it insures a tight nesting of the ten coils. For this reason, the vent pipe nut must be pulled up tightly. A loosely nesting set of coils will cause too great a difference between the condensate and feed temperatures, allowing excessive heat loss in the condensate, and making it impossible to operate with the proper amount of overflow.

o. *Heaters.* Install heater connections.

p. *Braces.* Install the braces at the bottom of the unit.

q. *Connections.* Connect all piping.

5C7. Final testing of reassembled unit. The final testing is done as follows:

a. *Test for leaks.* Start the feed pump and fill the unit with water until it appears at the overflow cup. Check the center and lower flanges for leaks, also the packing gland nuts and the bottom of the unit and threads where electric heaters are inserted. Test the heaters to determine whether or not all are working, by noting the readings on the ammeter.

NOTE. Do not install lagging until the unit operates without leaking.

b. *Insulation.* Install insulation and check heaters again to insure that all are connected properly.

5C8. Repairing coils. Any possible damage to the coils will require the use of silver solder. Cracks occasionally are found in the brazing. Proper brazing equipment and an expert mechanic are required for this work.

6

DESCRIPTION OF THE
MODEL X-1 DISTILLING UNIT

A. INTRODUCTION

6A1. Distiller types. At the date of this revision (Jan. 1955) there are several different types and models of distilling systems installed on submarines. They are:

a. Badger Model X-1, 1,000 GPD Vapor Compression Distilling Units. Two (2) units installed on each of the fleet type submarines and, with various alterations, on many of the snorkel submarines.

b. Badger Model V-1, 1,000 GPD Vapor Compression Distilling Units. Two (2) units installed on some of the later submarines, (SS563–568).

c. Badger Model WS-1, 300 GPD Vapor Compression Distilling Units. One (1) unit installed on each "T" class submarine.

d. Cleaver-Brooks, 300 GPD Vapor Compression Distilling Units. One (1) unit installed on each of the "K" class submarines.

e. Badger Model Y-1, 1,000 GPD Vapor Compression Distilling Units. Two (2) units installed on SSN type submarines.

f. Griscom-Russell, 4,000 GPD low pressure two effect, soloshell type Distilling Unit. One (1) unit installed on SSN type submarines.

All of these units, with the exception of soloshell type, operate on the same basic principles, and since it is beyond the scope of this text to describe them all in detail, the Model X-1 has been selected as typical. It differs from the others only in minor details.

In the later sections of this text some of these differences will be described.

6A2. Model X-1. The Model X-1 vapor compression distilling unit is rated at 1,000 gallons of distilled water per day. It will produce 50 to 60 gallons of distilled water per hour from about 70 to 90 gallons per hour of normal sea water. The temperature of the distillate will be within 18° F. of that of the sea water feed. The overflow will be about 30° above the feed temperature. The unit was primarily designed to make cleaning more convenient.

Its main advantages over other models are:

a. It has a larger capacity.

b. It runs longer without cleaning.

c. It makes better battery water since it is constructed of nonferrous material, with the exception of ¾-inch tubes in the heat exchanger, which are copper-nickel and tinned to prevent the contamination of condensate with nickel.

d. Its feed is inside the tubes; steam is outside the tubes.

e. It has short straight tubes. (This unit was designed originally to employ a mechanical cleaning method instead of acid cleaning. Submarines were equipped with mechanical cleaning equipment, and for a number of years the mechanical method of cleaning was the only method in common usage; now however, acid cleaning is used almost entirely, and it is expected that the mechanical cleaning gear will be deleted from the ship's allowance.)

f. It has an improved venting system.

g. It has more efficient auxiliary devices for control.

6A3. Difference between Model S and Model X-1 distilling units. The distillation process is the same in both units, the only difference being in mechanical design. In the Model S unit, the part played by the cones of coiled tubing, called the *heat exchanger*, is as follows:

a. Warming the feed.

b. Vaporizing the feed.

c. Condensing the vapor.

d. Cooling the condensate.

In the Model X-1 unit, the actions b and c are performed inside the main unit or evaporator in a space called the *steam chest*; actions a and d are performed in an external heat exchanger. Figure 6-1 is a cutaway view of the Model X-1 unit

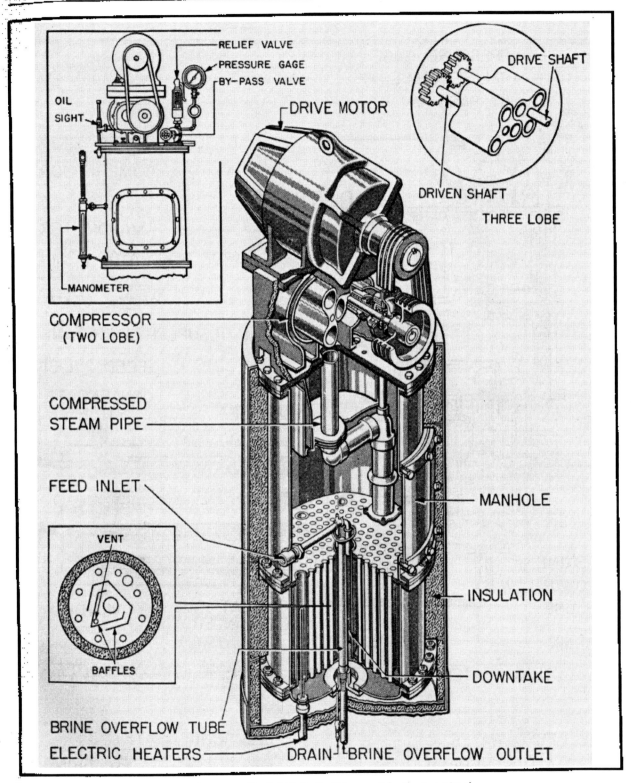

Figure 6-1. Model X-1 distilling unit (cutaway view).

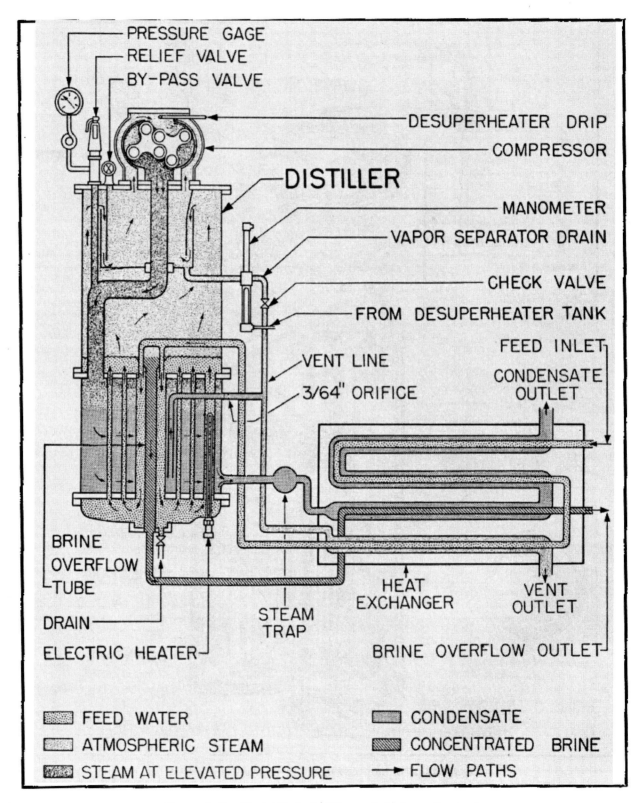

Figure 6–2. Model X–1 distilling unit (schematic view).

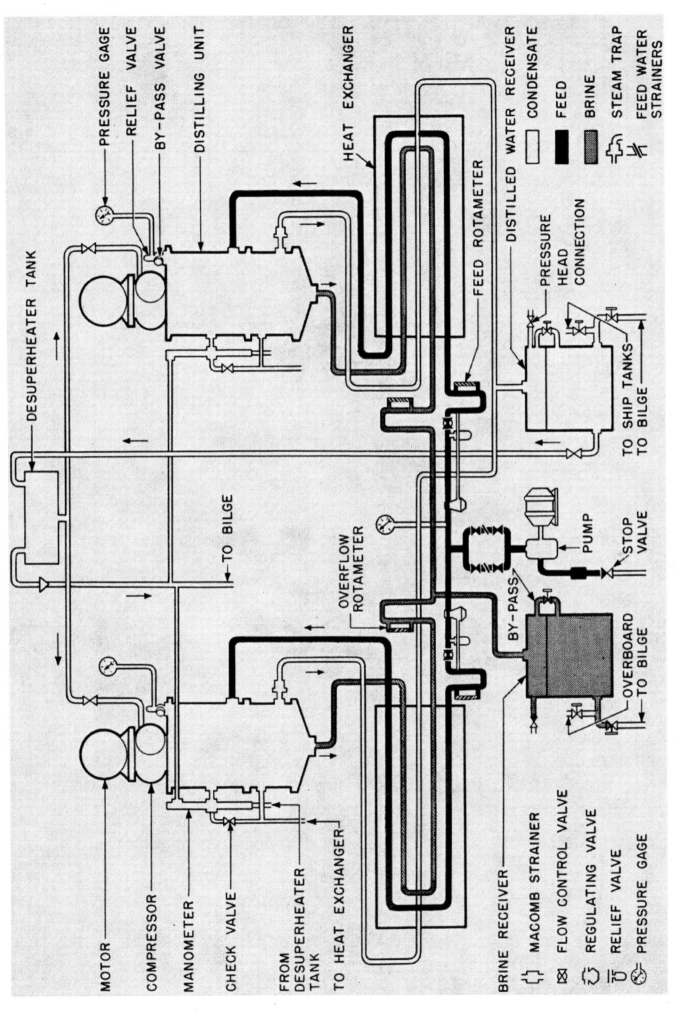

PRESSURE GAGE
RELIEF VALVE
BY-PASS VALVE
DISTILLING UNIT

HEAT EXCHANGER

FEED ROTAMETER

DISTILLED WATER RECEIVER

PRESSURE HEAD CONNECTION

CONDENSATE
FEED
BRINE
STEAM TRAP
FEED WATER STRAINERS

DESUPERHEATER TANK

TO BILGE

OVERFLOW ROTAMETER

TO SHIP TANKS
TO BILGE

PUMP

STOP VALVE

BY-PASS

OVERBOARD
TO BILGE

MOTOR
COMPRESSOR
MANOMETER
CHECK VALVE
FROM DESUPERHEATER TANK
TO HEAT EXCHANGER

BRINE RECEIVER

MACOMB STRAINER
FLOW CONTROL VALVE
REGULATING VALVE
RELIEF VALVE
PRESSURE GAGE

Figure 6-3. Piping arrangement, Model X-1 distilling plant two units.

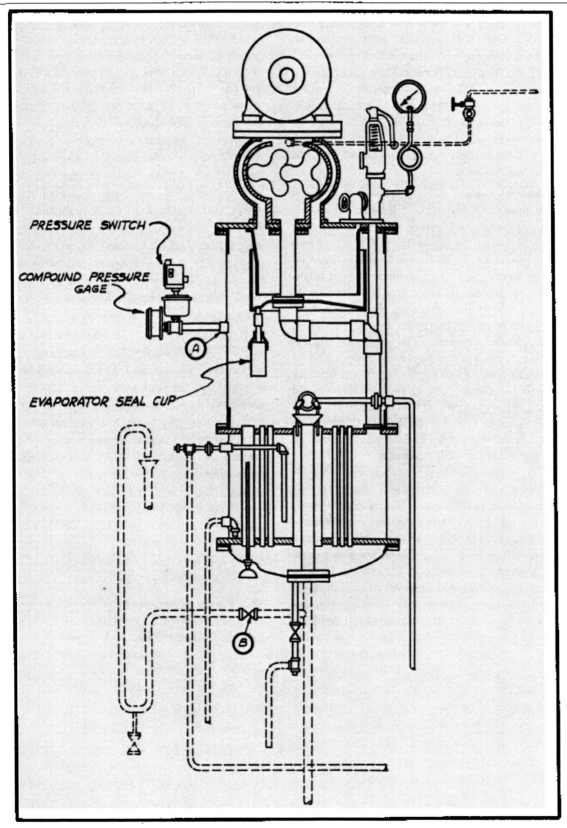

Figure 6–4. Schematic sketch for conversion of vapor compression distilling unit.

evaporator, while Figure 6–2 is a schematic diagram of a unit with external heat exchanger. The heat exchanger is illustrated in Figure 7–5.

The Model X–1 unit consists of two main parts—the *evaporator* and the *heat exchanger*. The evaporator can be subdivided into three main elements—the *steam chest; vapor separator;* and the *vapor compressor.* The heat exchanger is essentially a double-pipe heater connected to the evaporator by piping.

6A4. Flow of water. (See Figure 6–2.) With the unit operating, the cycle will be as follows:

Cold sea water feed enters the heat exchanger where it is heated to about 190°–200° F. From there it goes into the evaporator and is injected down the downcomer. In the downcomer it mixes with the recirculating water and is heated to its boiling point. It then flows up the ¾-inch tube where ½ to ⅔ of the incoming feed is vaporized at atmospheric pressure. The saturated atmospheric steam rises in the vapor chamber. The ½ to ⅓ of the feed remaining as liquid continually flows into the funnel, out of the evaporator and into the heat exchanger. This concentrated brine overflow is about 214° F. As it flows through the heat exchanger it gives up its heat and is cooled to within 30° F. of the cold sea water.

The atmospheric steam passes through the vapor separator where any entrainment separates out and is vented from the evaporator through a check valve except in those units equipped with conversions for operating with variable hull pressures. Where installed, this conversion substitutes a compound gage and pressure-static switch for the manometer, and the entrainment from the vapor separator is drained internally through a brass seal cup, and overflows with the brine. (See Figure 6–4.)

The manometer (or compound gage) indicate pressure inside the vapor separator, which is main tained at about atmospheric, except in the case of conversions. The atmospheric steam then goe into the suction of the compressor where distille water is dropped onto the rotating impellers t desuperheat the steam as it is compressed. Th compressed, saturated steam is discharged a about 3 psi for a clean unit, through a pipe to th steam chest, into the space on the outside of th ¾-inch tubes. As the 3-psi saturated steam con denses on the outside of the ¾-inch tubes it drop down and collects on the bottom tube plate. Ever time a pound of compressed steam condenses, ap proximately a pound of atmospheric steam i formed, thus keeping the compressor suction sup plied with the correct amount of steam.

The condensate is drawn off through a steam trap and flows into the heat exchanger at about 220° F. As it flows through the exchanger, it gives up its heat to the feed and is cooled to within about 18° of the cold water feed. The steam trap prevents any steam from leaving the evaporator and automatically maintains the compressor discharge pressure at exactly the correct pressure so that all the steam compressed will condense in the evaporator, regardless of the conditions of the heating surfaces. Any air or noncondensable gases are vented from the steam chest through a small orifice. This air, plus a small amount of steam, flows into the vent line, carrying the entrainment into the heat exchanger. The steam condenses and gives up its heat to the feed.

6A5. Piping arrangement of Model X–1 distilling unit. The complete functioning of the Model X–1 distilling plant is shown in Figure 6–3.

7

MECHANICAL DETAILS OF THE MODEL X-1 DISTILLING UNITS

A. GENERAL DESCRIPTION

7A1. Main unit or evaporator. This part of the distilling system is referred to as the *evaporator* because it is therein that the boiling and condensing, that is, actual distillation, takes place. The evaporator, exclusive of compressor and motor, is cylindrical in shape, with a 12- × 15-inch manhole opening into the space above the tubes of the steam chest. This cylindrical shell is covered with a thick layer of glass wool insulation held in place by a stainless steel jacket.

7A2. Steam chest. Inside the insulated jacket the lower part of the cylinder is the steam chest, where the sea water is vaporized, and distilled water condensed. It consists of 334 admiralty metal tubes, each 16¼ inches long with a ¾-inch o. d. These tubes are set side by side, as shown in Figure 6-1, and enclosed in a shell. At the top and bottom of the shell, the ends of these tubes are expanded into holes in the tube sheets.

Standing among the tubes are two angular sheet brass baffles 14¼ inches high. A pipe leads horizontally into the steam chest about 2½ inches from the top and bends down into the corner of the inner baffle extending to 2 inches from the bottom. This section of pipe, called the *steam chest vent*, is pierced with nineteen 1/16 inch holes, in two rows staggered along the side toward the open part of the baffle. The baffles cause any noncondensable gases such as air to flow to the closed end of the inner baffle, where they pass out through the steam chest vent. See also Section 7A9.

The steam chest also contains the electric heaters, center downtake pipe, and overflow pipe.

7A3. Electric heaters. (See Figure 3-1.) The eight electric heaters are contained in eight 1¾-inch tubes which are spaced equally around the outer diameter of the tube area of the steam chest. The feed flows through these tubes, coming in contact with the heaters.

7A4. Downtake. In the center of the bundle of tubes is a 4-inch pipe with ends expanded into the tube sheets. This is called the *downtake*. The feed enters the evaporator through a pipe above the steam chest, passing down through the downtake where it comes in contact with the concave head which is bolted to the bottom of the steam chest. The concave head is watertight, hence the feed cannot pass beyond it. As more feed is supplied through the downtake pipe, it floods up through the 342 tubes.

7A5. Feed. The feed inlet pipe in the evaporator extends horizontally to the center and there branches into a Y, the two ends of which turn down and extend just below the funnel (Figure 6-1). The Y-ends actually pass through the funnel wall. The newly incoming feed pours into the downtake, mixing with the vaporized portion of the feed already in the steam chest.

7A6. Overflow. The overflow is a 1¾-inch o. d. pipe which is inserted inside the downtake (Figure 6-2). At the top of this overflow pipe is brazed a 4-inch funnel. The top of the funnel is 2 inches above the top of the steam chest, maintaining the liquid level in the evaporator at this height. The overflow pipe leads out through the bottom of the evaporator to the heat exchanger, where it gives up its heat, raising the temperature of the incoming feed.

7A7. Portion of sea water distilled. About one-half to two-thirds of the feed is vaporized. The remaining one-third overflows continuously into the funnel, flowing out of the evaporator to the heat exchanger giving up its heat to the incoming feed water. From there it goes to the brine receiver where it is drained to bilges or blown to sea.

7A8. Vapor separator. The vapor separator is an interior compartment, as in the Model S unit, containing similar baffles (Figure 6–2). The vapor, entering at the top of the separator, descends between the walls, and enters the separator chamber from where it travels upward to the compressor suction.

This circuitous passage of vapor causes any mist of liquid that may be carried up by the vigorous boiling action to *separate* from the vapor and fall on the separator floor. In the original installations, the separated water drains out through the separator drain pipe, manometer, and a check valve into the evaporator vent pipe and thence through the heat exchanger into the bilges. In the units which have been altered for operation while snorkeling, the drain from the separator runs into a brass seal cup inside the unit and overflows with the brine.

In the original fleet type installations, the water boils at substantially atmospheric pressure inside the vessel. The contact with the atmosphere is through the separator drain pipe and manometer. The manometer (to be described later) is an instrument which indicates the pressure of the steam in the vapor separator. If the pressure indicated is above or below that found in the vessel, adjustment of the heaters and/or the feed must be made.

In the converted units (see Figure 6–4) there is no vent from the vapor space inside the unit to the external pressure. The vapor pressure of the boiling water is registered on a compound gage which registers either vacuum (inches of Mercury) or pressure (inches of water). There is a pressure-static switch connected to the gage piping which is set to automatically control four (4) heating elements to maintain the vapor pressure at a positive pressure between six (6) and twelve (12) inches of pressure.

This arrangement minimizes the effect of variable hull pressures on the operation of the unit.

7A9. The steam chest vent. A pipe leads horizontally into the steam chest about $2\frac{1}{2}$ inches from the top and extends down into the steam chest to within 2 inches of the bottom. This section of pipe, called the *steam chest vent*, is pierced with nineteen $\frac{1}{16}$-inch holes, in two rows staggered along the side toward the open part of the baffle, as described in Section 7A2.

In this horizontal branch pipe, just outside the evaporator, is a union. Inside the pipe at this point is a 100-mesh strainer and a diaphragm with a $\frac{3}{64}$-inch hole or orifice bored in its center. The purpose of this small orifice is to vent air (which is not condensable) from the steam chest. Normally only a very small amount of air is present, hence the orifice is made small. The diaphragm also prevents any drainage from the vapor separator drain pipe and manometer from entering the distilled water through the steam chest vent, in the case of the units still not converted. See Section 7A8.

7A10. Steam trap. The condensate in flowing from the evaporator to the heat exchanger passes through the steam trap. The steam trap prevents any steam from flowing from the steam chest into the heat exchanger. In so doing, it automatically keeps the compressor discharge pressure at the required value, sufficient to raise the condensation point of the vapor and thus produce condensation in the steam chest, regardless of the condition of the heat transfer surface. Pressure within the steam chest is necessary to provide a head against which the compressor can work.

The steam trap takes the place of, and serves the same purpose as the retarders in the Model S unit.

The steam trap is of conventional type, roughly spherical in shape, $4\frac{3}{4}$ inches inside diameter. The condensate water enters horizontally at one side and leaves at a point diametrically opposite. The outlet is a short tubular extension with a flat bolted cover, holding the connection and working parts. The inside dimension horizontally from inlet to cover plate is $5\frac{1}{8}$ inches.

Normally the steam trap is about half full of condensate (water), the level of which is at the top of the inlet opening. A spherical float connected by lever action to a pin valve in the outlet, rises and falls with the condensate level, permitting the condensate to flow out only as fast as it flows into the trap.

The action of the steam trap is as follows: The condensate leaving the steam chest contains some uncondensed steam mixed with it. In the steam trap, the condensate fills only the lower half of the enclosed space. The upper half is steam space. When the water drops below its normal level the float drops with it, shuts the outlet valve, and remains shut until the water level again rises. There is a permanent bypass around the valve of the steam trap, from the vapor chamber to the outlet pipe. This bypass is $\frac{1}{32}$ inch in diameter at its smallest point and serves to prevent the trap from becoming air bound. Before the bypass valve on the distiller is shut, air is discharged through the trap. If the permanent bypass is plugged, the trap must be manually vented before the unit will operate. On the top of the trap there is a small valve which can be opened manually to vent off large quantities of air.

The condensate normally flows from the steam chest as it is formed. When the flow of condensate is restricted, pressure will build up in the steam chest. This may be caused by the float being stuck in the closed position or the orifice in the bypass being plugged. If this condition occurs, vent air from the steam trap by hand; if the pressure comes down and gradually builds up, it is a good indication that the trap is not operating properly. The unit should be secured and the steam trap repaired.

7A11. Pressure gage. A 0- to 15-psi pressure gage (Figure 3-3) is connected in the vapor compressor discharge line. The compressor pressure gage indicates the discharge pressure of the compressor and the pressure at which the compressed steam condenses on the outside of the tubes of the steam chest.

Abnormal compressor discharge pressure is the first indication of trouble. The normal compressor discharge pressure varies with the speed of the compressor and the scale conditions inside the tubes of the steam chest where the sea water is vaporized. At constant compressor speed the compressor discharge pressure is a direct indication of the amount of scale in the evaporator.

7A12. Relief valve. A relief valve (Figure 3-6) is located on the upper head plate adjacent to the compressor. It connects into the vapor compressor discharge line and prevents overloading of the compressor motor. The valve is normally closed under spring pressure set at $7\frac{1}{2}$ psi. It can also be manually opened at any time by lifting the lever. It is a safety valve, not a control valve.

7A13. Feed pump. The main sea water supply to the unit is provided by a centrifugal type motor-driven feed pump, capable of delivering 3 to 4 gallons per minute at 30 to 40 pounds gage pressure. The feed may also be from the variable ballast tanks, or from the fresh water supply.

7A14. Water tanks. a. *Distilled water.* The distilled water, from both units, flows into a *distilled water receiver* or tank (Figure 6-3), made of nonferrous metal, of approximately 46-gallon capacity. Air at 10 psi is admitted at the top of the tank to give a head pressure. A petcock is provided for sampling. There is also a vent and a drain to the bilge. Piping connections lead to the desuperheater tank, to the battery water system, and to the ship's fresh water system.

b. *Brine receiver.* The overflow of concentrated brine flows from the heat exchanger to a brine receiver or tank, made of copper nickel, of approximately 23-gallon capacity. Air at 30 psi is admitted at the top of the tank to provide a head when discharging overboard. There is a vent and a drain to the bilge. The drain to the bilge has a side-swing connection leading either overboard or to fresh water storage when feeding fresh water.

B. THE THREE-LOBED GENERAL MOTORS COMPRESSOR

7B1. Description. The General Motors vapor compressor is of the positive displacement type consisting of two rotors enclosed in a special compact housing designed for mounting on evaporators.

Each rotor has three helical lobes designed to produce a continuous uniform flow of vapor. The vapor enters the compressor housing at the bottom and passes upward between the inner and outer walls to the rotor chamber where it fills the spaces between the rotor lobes as they roll apart. This vapor is then carried by the rotors in the spaces between the lobes around the cylindrical sides of the housing, producing a pressure at the bottom as the lobes roll together. Clearance is provided to prevent the rotors from touching each other or the surrounding housing.

7B2. Impeller gears. Opposite to the drive end, a pair of one-to-one precision helical gears turns the other impeller. The impeller gears run in an oil bath in an oiltight housing. The shafts pass through packing glands in the housing.

7B3. Lubrication. The compressor is lubricated from two reservoirs, one at each end. Each oil reservoir is supplied with an oil level indicator, which is attached to the compressor housing. The oil level should be checked every 24 hours and oil added as needed when the compressor is not running. The oil should be changed when the evaporator is cleaned.

Two vertical ½-inch nipples closed with pipe caps (Figure 9–1, 89) are provided for filling the oil compartments. Remove the pipe caps and pour the oil into the nipples until the proper level is reached on the gage.

The oil may be drained from the compartments by opening the ½-inch plug cocks (Figure 9–1, 17).

Oil is retained in the oil compartments by the use of slinger rings (Figure 9–1, 33 and 34) and steam leakage is prevented by the use of stuffing box glands (51 and 53).

These glands should be adjusted so that they will be just tight enough to prevent leakage. Excessive tightness will damage the packing and shaft sleeves, causing excessive heating and the impellers to stick. The gland nuts must be tightened evenly.

The reservoir of oil at the pulley end of the compressor lubricates the ball bearings by a slinger attached to the driven shaft. The reservoir of oil at the opposite end from the pulley lubricates the timing gears and ball bearings at that end of the compressor by the splashing of the gears.

7B4. Steam packing. When steam leakage cannot be stopped by tightening the glands, new packing must be installed. This may be done without dis-

mantling the compressor. First loosen the nuts and back out the gland (Figure 9–1, piece 53).

Each stuffing box is packed with five rings of Johns-Manville No. 350.

Remove all five packing rings, using the packing hook found in the spare parts box. Install five rings of No. 350 packing and install the gland. Tighten gradually and evenly as recommended.

The split packing gland may be removed from the shaft during the packing operation if it is found necessary.

7B5. Compressor motor. A 7½-hp motor with necessary starting and protective electrical equipment is bolted on top of the compressor casing. The drive to the compressor shaft pulley is by four texrope V-belts.

7B6. Variable pitch drive. The drive pulley on the motor is of the adjustable or variable pitch type. The amount of variation of pitch is small—5.400 to 6.600 inches pitch diameter of the pulley—and is intended only to adjust the tension of the belts. The four left-hand sides of the pulley grooves are attached to a sliding sleeve. Rotating this sleeve moves the left-hand sides toward or away from the four stationary right-hand sides. Since the belt grooves are V-shaped in section, this motion increases or decreases the pitch diameter.

Adjusting the variable pitch drive. Loosen the setscrews on the sleeve. Turn the adjustable part of the pulley with the special spanner wrench (found in the spare parts box) until the belts are at proper tension. The proper tension is that which gives the belts, when running, a bow of about an inch on the slack side. Then tighten the setscrews.

C. CONTROL DEVICES ON MODEL X–1 DISTILLING UNIT

7C1. Manometer. The manometer (Figure 7–1) is used on the units which have not been converted for operation while snorkeling. It consists essentially of a brass framework holding two glass tubes, one tube within the other. The *inner* tube is smaller in diameter and approximately twice the length of the *outer* tube. The outer and larger tube is closed at the bottom and at the top it has two openings, one of which is connected to the drain from the vapor separator, the other being the manometer drain to the heat exchanger. The smaller or *inner* tube supported by the framework,

is open at both ends. The lower end is inside, near the bottom of the larger tube; the upper end projects out of the top of the outer tube and is open to the atmosphere.

During the time that the distiller is in operation the manometer contains a small amount of water normally supplied by drainage from the vapor separator. During the warming-up period, some water is drawn out of the manometer into the vapor separator. Just prior to the time that the distiller is ready to be cut in, the manometer should be filled to its normal operating level, which is at the top of the outer glass, with water from the desuperheater tank. A pipe connection and valve are provided near the bottom of the

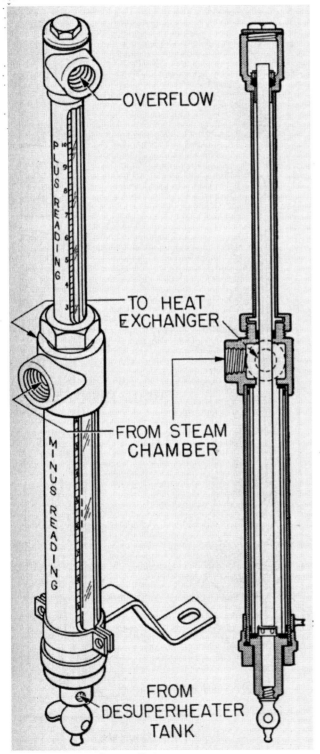

Figure 7-1. Manometer.

OVERFLOW

TO HEAT EXCHANGER

FROM STEAM CHAMBER

FROM DESUPERHEATER TANK

PLUS READING

MINUS READING

manometer for this purpose. While the distiller is in operation the upper surface of the water in the *outer* glass tube is subjected to the pressure from the vapor separator. This pressure may be either above or below atmospheric pressure. Since the upper end of the *inner* glass tube is open, the water in the inner tube is subjected to two forces: the vapor pressure caused by the boiling water in the distiller, and atmospheric pressure. The reading of the manometer is obtained by determining the difference in water level in the two tubes.

When the level in the small inner tube is above the level in the large outer tube, the pressure in the evaporator is above atmospheric. When the level in the small tube is below the level in the large tube, the pressure in the evaporator is below atmospheric. If the large tube is completely full, its level is at zero and the pressure in the evaporator is indicated directly in inches of water by the level in the small tube on the manometer scale.

The manometer is the primary guide in operating the unit, since it indicates exactly how the unit is balanced. The manometer level remains constant if the unit is in exact balance. When the unit is operating properly, the reading level is behind the collar holding the vapor inlet. If the reading level becomes visible above or below this collar, the unit should be adjusted. On units converted for operation with variable hull pressures, the manometer has been replaced with a pressure actuated switch and a compound gage. (See paragraph 7A8.) (See also Figure 6–4.)

7C2. The rotameter. Two of these devices are used for each distilling unit (Figure 7–2). One is inserted in the incoming sea water line into the heat exchanger to measure the rate of the feed flow, which is normally 70 to 90 gph. The other is in the outlet pipe from the heat exchanger to the brine receiver to measure the rate of overflow, which is approximately ⅓ to ½ of the total feed.

The rotameter is an upright pyrex glass tube about 14 inches long (exclusive of end fittings) through which the water flows. A metal casing with a plexiglas window protects it. The tube is tapered, with the small end at the bottom. Inside, a small metal *rotor* with a central hole slides up and down on a guide rod, and is caused to spin for free sliding by small vanes cut into its sides. Since the tube is tapered, the space between the rotor and the tube wall increases as the rotor rises, permitting more water to flow through that space. Therefore, the rotor will always rise to a height corresponding to the rate of flow at any particular time. A scale on the tube reads directly in gallons per hour.

7C3. Bypass valve. This valve (Figure 7–3) on the Model X–1 unit is located on top of the upper head plate. It is not built into the head plate as in the Model S unit, but is an individual device, bolted on. It is a stop valve and when open, it permits the compressor discharge to return directly into the vapor separator. It is opened when starting, and closed during distillation.

7C4. Feed regulating and flow control valves. In the feed line, just after the water filters leading to the heat exchanger, is the feed regulating valve (Figure 7–4) and the flow control valve (Figure 3–9). These valves control the flow of incoming feed water. The flow control valve is set to give any desired flow through the feed rotameter. The regulating valve then maintains the feed constant at this rate regardless of feed pressure changes.

The flow control or feed valve is used as a variable orifice. Any similar type valve could be substituted but the adjustment is much finer if a flow control type is used.

The regulating valve is a spring-loaded diaphragm type valve, similar to an ordinary reducing valve, having two watertight compartments separated by the diaphragm. It is installed with the spring and diaphragm below the feed line. Connecting into the feed line is a ball type valve with the lower or discharge side open to the compartment on top of the diaphragm and open to the feed line just before the flow control valve. The diaphragm acts on the ball to open or close the ball valve. The water pressure present just before the flow valve, is exerted downward on the diaphragm and tends to close the ball valve by displacing the diaphragm downward. The compartment below the diaphragm is connected into the feed line just after the flow control valve. A coil spring in this lower compartment exerts a pressure upward on the diaphragm equivalent to 5 psi in addition to whatever pressure is present in the feed line just after the flow control valve. Thus the pressure in the feed line just before the flow control valve will always be exactly 5 psi more than the pressure in the feed line just after the

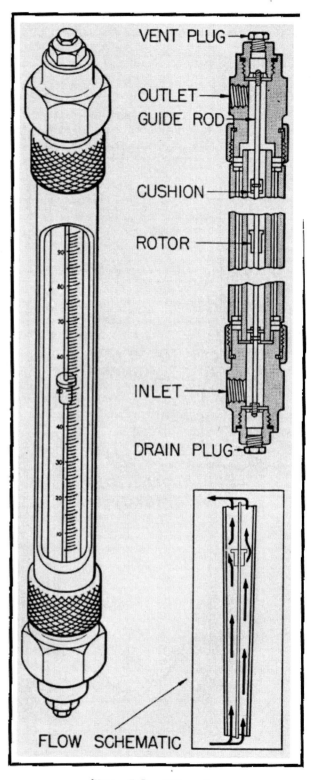

Figure 7-2. Rotameter.

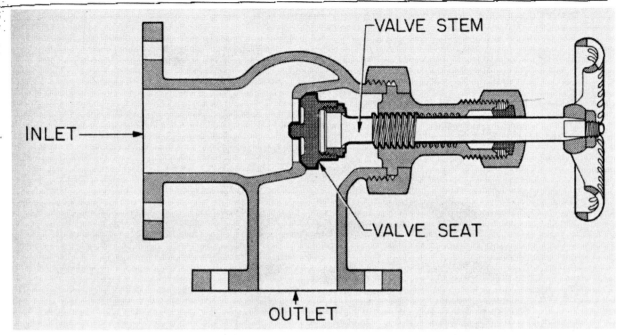

Figure 7-3. Bypass valve.

flow control valve. Once the flow control is set at any given opening, the flow through it will remain constant because of the constant pressure drop through it, regardless of pressure fluctuations in the feed line before the regulating valve or after the flow control valve.

The small spring on top of the ball serves to keep the ball in place.

7C5. Other valves in the feed line. Between the regulating and flow control valves, a relief valve set at 50 psi is connected into the feed line of each unit. A feed pump discharge gage is set into the line beyond the feed water filters and indicates the feed pressure just before the regulating valve.

7C6. Order of devices in the feed line. The devices of the feed line, starting from the hull, are as follows: stop valve, Macomb strainer, feed pump, filters (two), feed pump discharge pressure gage, feed regulating valve, relief valve, flow control valve, and feed rotameter.

D. THE DESUPERHEATER

7D1. Desuperheater. An 8-gallon *desuperheater tank*, fed by a pipe from the distilled water tank (Figure 6-3), is supported above the units. A water level gage is attached to the desuperheater tank, and an overflow pipe leads to the bilge. From the bottom of the desuperheater tank, a ¼-inch tube leads to each of the compressors and into the impeller housings above the impellers. Valves in these tubes are adjusted to cause the distilled water to flow as drops, not as a steady stream on the impeller lobes. Since the drip is inside the compressors and hence not visible, a *sight feed glass* with a glass window through which the water drops may be seen passing, is inserted in each tube just

outside the compressor. In normal operation of the units, the desuperheater flow is at a rate of 200 drops or more per minute. A rate of 200 drops per minute is a very rapid one. It is the rate that exists just before the flow becomes a steady stream in the sight glass.

7D2. Need for desuperheating. When steam generated by boiling liquid at atmospheric pressure and a temperature of 212° F. is compressed mechanically to a pressure between 3 to 6 pounds, the steam is superheated and reaches a temperature of 285° to 400° F. in the compressor. If this compression takes place in the presence of water, the water removes the superheat from the steam and

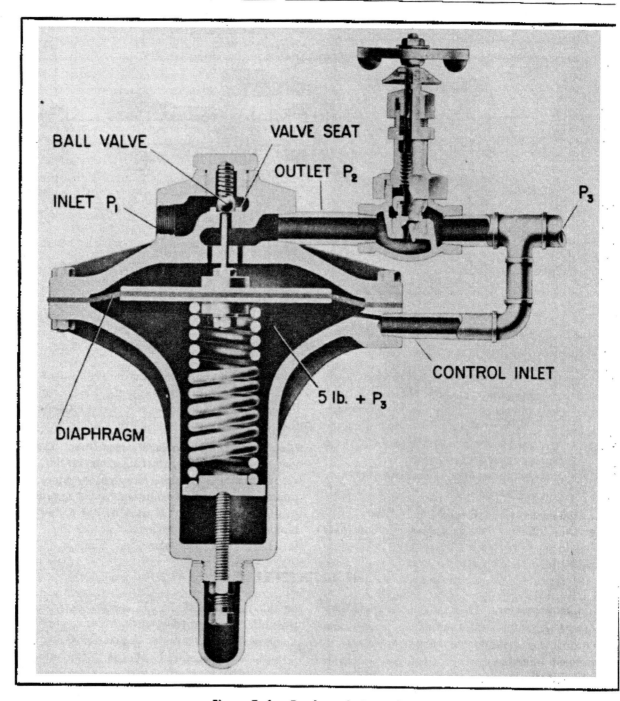

Figure 7–4. Feed regulating valve.

allows it to pass into the distiller at a temperature of saturated steam, which is 222° F. at 3 pounds and 230° F. at 6 pounds gage. Desuperheating is needed for two purposes:

a. Water from the desuperheater tank dripping on the impellers keeps the impellers and their shafts. cooled. This cooling action prevents too great an expansion of the impellers by heat, thus retaining the required clearance of the impellers. It also prevents the shaft packing from getting too hot, which would cause rapid deterioration of the packing.

b. Better heat transfer is obtained from saturated steam than from superheated steam. A fast heat transfer is necessary to assist in keeping the feed water boiling; the quicker the steam condenses, the lower the pressure on the discharge side of the compressor will be.

Distilled water must be used for this desuperheating process. Ordinary fresh water contains various minerals and chemical compounds. These substances, while harmless to human health, would be deposited on the impellers (since only the water vaporizes) and would gradually build up to a thickness that would cause the impellers to bind.

E. HEAT EXCHANGER

7E1. Heat exchanger. The feed heat exchanger is a preheater which warms the incoming sea water feed. The sea water enters at ocean temperature, which varies according to location and season. It leaves the heat exchanger at about 200° F. Hence, when the feed enters the evaporator, it needs to be raised only a few degrees more to reach the boiling point. The construction of this heat exchanger, and a diagram of the flow paths through it are shown in Figure 7-5.

The distilled water or condensate leaving the steam chest reenters the heat exchanger, at about the same temperature as the condensing steam in the steam chest (220° F. at 3 psi), passing countercurrent (that is, in the opposite direction) to the feed flow, in order to assure the best heat transfer from the hot outgoing distilled water to the cool incoming feed, and thus warming the feed and cooling the distillate or condensate. The heat exchanger is of the double tube type. It consists of fifty 1¼-inches i. d., straight tubes, 45 inches long; and fifty ¾-inch o. d., straight tubes, 48 inches long. The ¾-inch tubes are externally finned with No. 18 gage copper nickel wire. There are also six tube sheets, three on each end. In the assembly of the heat exchanger, the large tubes are arranged in a bank and inserted in the inner tube sheets (Figure 7-5); the tubes are packed into these tube sheets with fiber and metallic packing to prevent leakage.

CAUTION. The metallic packing should not be installed so that it is in contact with the fresh water or condensate side of the heat exchanger.

The small tubes have their ends silver-soldered into a bushing at each end. This assembly is inserted inside the larger tubes. The ends of the small tubes with the bushing extend out of the larger tubes about 1½ inches on each end and through the outer tube sheets. The bushing is packed into these tube sheets. The tube sheet cover plates seal the ends of the heat exchanger. The outer tube sheets and the tube sheet cover plates contain milled passages which direct the flow of water. The entire tube bundle is enclosed in a brass casing for protection.

7E2. Flow paths in the heat exchanger. There are four distinct flow paths through the heat exchanger. The condensate flows through 48 large tubes, around the smaller tubes. Steam from the vent pipe and drainage from the vapor separator flow through two large tubes around the smaller tubes. Feed water flows through 36 of the small tubes. The brine overflow from the steam chest flows through 14 of the small tubes. The flow in the large tubes is in the space left around the small tubes. The small tubes are connected by return headers at each end, and in such a way as to provide two separate longer paths of water flow. The large tubes are likewise connected by return headers at each end in such a way as to provide two separate longer paths of water flow, each completely separate from the others.

The flow diagrams in the lower right corner of Figure 7-5 show these four separate paths. The diagrams show the pipes as viewed from the inlet and looking toward the rear or return end; that is, the pipes are represented as circles. In order to describe the flow paths in a simple manner, the tubes are designated in accordance with the following plan.

The rows are designated by letters starting with the top row. Capital letters refer to the large tubes. Small letters refer to the ¾-inch o. d. tubes. The tubes in each row are designated by numbers from 1 to 6 starting at the right. In the diagram only the top row has the numbers; each row is similarly designated, starting from the right. Two diagrams are used in order to simplify the presentation of the four paths. In the following description, the term *goes forward*

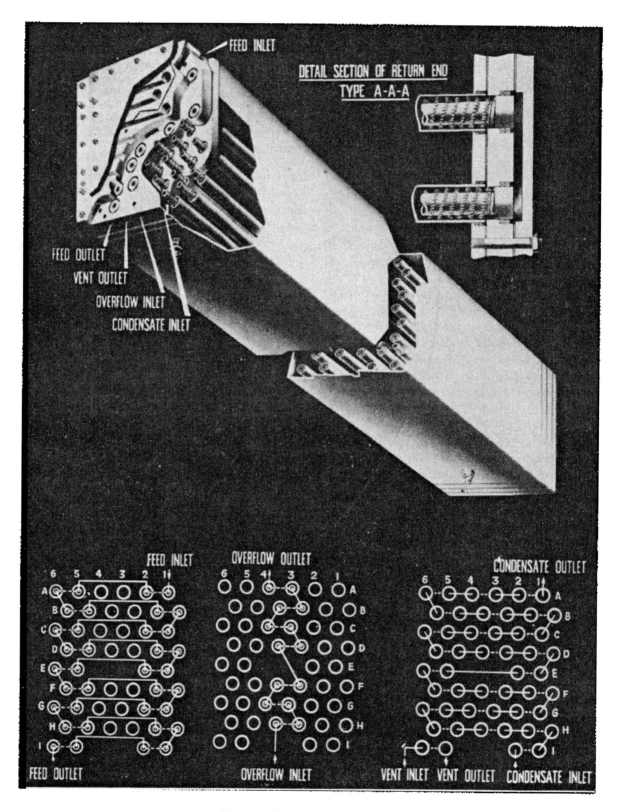

Figure 7–5.   Heat exchanger.

means that the flow is away from the observer as he looks at the flow diagrams in Figure 7–5; that is, from the inlet and toward the return end. The term *comes back* means that the flow is in the opposite direction; that is, toward the observer, or from the return end to the inlet end. When it is said that the flow goes forward in a1, comes back in a2, it is naturally understood that the flow crosses from a1 to a2 in the return end header. When it is said that the flow comes back to a2, goes forward in a5, it is understood that the flow crosses from a2 to a5 in the inlet end header.

Feed flow. The feed flows through 36 small tubes, entering cold at the top of the heat exchanger. It goes forward in a1, comes back in a2, goes forward in a5, comes back in a6, goes forward in b6, comes back in b5, goes forward in b2, and comes back in b1. Continuing, it follows the same route in rows c, d, e, f, g, h, and i, emerging hot from tube i6 at the inlet end of the heat exchanger, as may be seen in Figure 7–5.

Overflow path. The hot brine overflow uses the remaining 14 small tubes, entering hot at the bottom of the heat exchanger. It goes forward in h4, comes back in h3, goes forward in g3, and comes back in g4. Continuing, it follows the same route, as may be seen in Figure 7–5, in rows f, e, c, b, and a, emerging cool from tube a4 at the inlet end of the heat exchanger.

Condensate path. The condensate flows in 48 of the large diameter tubes, entering hot at the bottom of the heat exchanger. It goes forward in I2, comes back in I1, goes forward in H1, comes back in H2, goes forward in H3, comes back in H4, goes forward in H5, comes back in H6, goes forward in G6, comes back in G5, goes forward in G4, comes back in G3, goes forward in G2, comes back in G1, and goes forward in F1. Continuing, it follows the same route, as may be seen in Figure 7–5, through the remaining rows. The condensate emerges cool from tube A1 at the inlet end of the heat exchanger.

Vent flow. Steam and noncondensable gases from the manometer and steam chest flow inside the remaining two large tubes in the bottom row, where the steam is condensed and the gases cooled. They enter hot and go forward in 16; and come back in 15, emerging somewhat cooled from tube 15 at the inlet end of the heat exchanger.

7E3. Step-wise heat transfer. It may be noted that the heat transfer takes place in a step-wise manner in the heat exchanger. The hot condensate gives up some heat to the feed in tubes I2, I1, H1, and H2; picks up a little heat from the overflow in G4, and G3; gives up heat to feed in G2, G1, F1, and F2; and continues this step-wise heat transfer throughout its path to A1. The loss of heat from condensate to feed, however, is always much greater than the gain of heat from overflow to condensate, so that the total result is a large heat transfer and overflow to feed.

8

OPERATION OF THE
MODEL X-1 DISTILLING UNIT

A. GENERAL PRINCIPLES

8A1. Heat supply. Heat is supplied to the unit two ways: one, by the work done by the compressor in compressing the steam, and the other by means of the electric heaters. The heat supplied by the electric heaters is proportional to the number of heaters turned on and can be varied at will by the operator. The energy supplied by the compressor cannot be changed at will by the operator. It depends on several conditions and changes as the conditions change. As the compressor discharge pressure increases, the energy input from the compressor increases. As the speed changes, the energy input changes. At a higher speed the compressor delivers more energy. However, only a small part of this increased energy, due to the increase in the compressor speed, is actually available because all the operating conditions change accordingly.

The heat supply is affected by the formation of scale. If the condition of scaling in the evaporator remained constant, the operation would be simple. But the scale accumulates on the boiling surfaces as operation continues, and decreases the heat transfer through the walls of the tubes between liquid and vapor. Normally a certain amount of the heat can be transferred; it remains in the compressed steam discharged from the compressor. The compressor discharge pressure therefore rises; which means that there is an increase in the heat input from the compressor.

8A2. Feed rate. The matter of feed rate is very important, and must be thoroughly understood in order to operate the unit correctly. The amount of heat which the feed can pick up depends on the rate at which it flows through the tubes of the heat exchanger and the steam chest of the evaporator. If the feed rate is slow, the water picks up more heat during that passage because it is longer in contact with the hot tubes. If the feed rate is fast, the water picks up less heat, for it has less time to do so.

Experience has shown that with this type of unit a minimum feed rate of 70 gph is necessary in order that the rate of scale formation may be kept low. The unit is designed, therefore, so that sufficient heat is supplied to maintain vaporization of the feed, normally at a minimum feed rate of 70 gph with a compressor speed of about 2,000 rpm. If the total heat supply decreases, so that boiling is stopped, it is possible to restart the boiling by slowing the feed rate. This, however, causes a material increase in the rate of scale formation and a high degree of salinity in the distiller. Lowering the feed rate under 70 gph is therefore not permissible, except perhaps in an emergency, and then only for a short period.

If the heat input to the unit drops, the proper remedy is to increase the heat input by turning on more electric heaters.

8A3. Heat loss. Heat is lost from the unit through the insulation and in the hot condensate and overflow streams. The condensate is at a constant temperature. Its rate of flow depends on the compressor speed and will be substantially constant at a given compressor speed. Hence the heat loss in the condensate stream is substantially constant. The overflow is also at a constant temperature, but its rate of flow depends on the feed rate. The heat loss in the overflow stream accordingly varies directly with the overflow rate or the feed rate.

8A4. Heat balance. If more heat is being supplied to the distiller than is required to balance the losses, more atmospheric pressure steam than the compressor requires will be generated. This will tend to build up a pressure above the feed in the evaporator and will cause the manometer pressure to rise. Increasing the feed rate will give more brine overflow, increase the heat loss, and make the manometer pressure stop rising and come down. Turning off the electric heaters would have the same effect in balancing the heat input against the losses.

NOTE. In this discussion, where ever reference is made to manometer pressure rising and falling, it is to be understood that some installations are fitted with a compound gage instead of a manometer. The pressure gage will register the same rise and fall in the vapor pressure as the manometer.

Should the heat losses be more than the energy input, an insufficient amount of atmospheric pressure steam will be generated. A partial vacuum will be produced in the vapor separator, that is, the pressure above the feed will decrease slightly and the reading in the manometer will fall. To correct this, the feed rate must be reduced or more electric heaters turned on.

This unit is operated and kept in balance solely by adjusting the feed rate and number of electric heaters in use, resulting in a sufficient amount of feed and a constant pressure level in the manometer.

The heat balance of the unit is very sensitive. All changes made in the operating conditions must be small and must be made slowly.

8A5. Automatic operation. The vapor compression distilling unit operates best when all conditions remain constant. If the voltage varies, the speed of the compressor and the corresponding output of the condensate change. This varying condition necessitates constant changes in feed rate or number of electric heaters used to keep the unit in perfect balance. With the old type installation (units employing a manometer instead of a pressure gage), under the above conditions, or in a heavy sea, the unit should be balanced with a manometer reading of plus 2 to 4 inches. The operator then has merely to check the manometer pressure and make a slight adjustment, if necessary, to the flow control valve every 15–30 minutes when transferring condensate from the test tanks to storage.

Under normal conditions, and in a moderate sea, when the voltage is constant, the unit may be balanced so that the manometer pressure is between plus 2 inches and minus 4 inches.

Changes in air pressure inside the submarine will also have an upsetting effect on the heat balance of the unit. On the fleet type submarine this was not a serious problem because there were

rarely any sudden or considerable pressure variations.

With the advent of the snorkel, varying hull pressures became an important consideration because air pressure changes while snorkeling sometimes are frequent and of sufficient magnitude to destroy the balance of an operating distilling plant. Since it is often necessary to run the distillers while snorkeling, conversion kits were supplied to the snorkel equipped submarines for installation on the distilling units. (See Figure 6–4.)

In this conversion, the manometer is eliminated and in its place a compound gage and pressure-static switch are installed. The gage serves the same purpose as the manometer, and the pressure actuated switch controls four of the eight heaters automatically to compensate for pressure fluctuations inside the hull.

The vent from the vapor separator to the atmosphere has been sealed off, and the pressure-static switch is set so that the pressure in the vapor space of the evaporator is maintained at between six and twelve inches of water. The entrainment separated from the vapor in the vapor separator runs into a seal cup inside the unit and flows away with the brine.

A stop valve has been installed in the evaporator level safety overflow line. This valve, when shut, prevents fluctuations in hull air pressure from being communicated to the interior of the evaporator through the brine overflow tube and funnel. The valve may be open or closed depending on the operation of the plant. It should be shut while snorkeling, but during such operations as acid cleaning or flushing it should be open because of the possibility of the normal brine piping becoming clogged at the heat exchanger. Usually the valve is opened when securing the plant, prior to flushing and left open until the units have been filled when placing the plant in operation (valve in question is valve "B" in Figure 6–4).

This conversion has largely overcome the problems caused by varying conditions and makes the operation of the distilling plants semi-automatic.

8A6. Continuous operation. For continuous operation, the unit should be secured every 24 hours and the oil levels in the compressor checked. It may be restarted immediately. If the unit is shut down more often, check the oil levels in the compressor before every start. Add oil when necessary.

A low feed pump discharge pressure indicates a dirty feed strainer. In such a case, switch to the other strainer and clean the dirty one. The strainers are located between the pump discharge and the gage.

8A7. Belts. As the belts wear and become loose, the variable pitch sheave on the compressor motor pulley must be tightened to take up excess slack in the belt. This increases the diameter of the pulley section in which the belts ride and gives a higher compressor speed. The maximum allowable speed of the compressor is limited only by the allowable motor overload. The speed of the compressor should not be such that the motor current exceeds 1.2 times its rated number of amperes as indicated on the motor nameplate.

8A8. Emergency operating. In an emergency, the unit may be operated longer than 500 hours without cleaning. However, when the compressor motor is overloaded by 20 percent as indicated by the ammeter, the unit must be secured and cleaned. Further operation may burn out the motor.

8A9. Distilling fresh water. Operating the unit on distilled fresh water for the last 10 to 20 hours from port, will tend to reduce the scale formation and will extend appreciably the number of hours between cleanings. The unit should be operated on fresh water in the same manner as it is on sea water.

B. STARTING THE MODEL X-1 DISTILLING UNIT

8B1. Starting routine. The following directions are for the Model X-1 (or Model AAA-1) distilling unit equipped with a G. M. 3 lobe helical compressor. Instructions for starting units converted for snorkel operation will be described in Section 8F.

a. Turn on the main power switch.

b. Line up the valves in the feed, condensate, brine overflow and vent lines.

c. Start the feed pump. Check the feed pressure gage, venting the feed pump if necessary. The minimum feed pressure is 25 pounds.

d. Open the feed flow control valve and observe the flow in the feed rotameter; adjust the feed so as to have a flow of 90 gph.

e. When the flow begins in the brine overflow rotameter, secure the flow control valve and the feed pump.

f. Turn on the electric heater switches, checking the ammeter as each switch is turned on.

CAUTION. The electric heaters will burn out unless covered with water. Do not turn on the electric heaters without first filling the unit with water, as evidenced by a flow in the brine overflow rotameter.

g. Check the following in preparation for starting the compressor motor:

Bypass valve. The bypass valve must always be fully open when the compressor is started.

Belts. Belts must have slack. Belts that are too tight will cause the compressor to bind and will overload the motor.

Desuperheater water. Check the water level in the tank. The tank should be at least half full.

Oil levels in compressor. Compressor oil levels must be midway in the sight glasses when the compressor is not running.

CAUTION. Use only Navy No. 9370 or SAE 40 oil in the compressor. Rheostat. Motors must always be started at the lowest speed with the rheostat all the way to the left.

h. Start the compressor motor 2 hours after turning on the electric heaters.

CAUTION. Check motor ampere reading. If it is greater than 1.2 times the rated motor current as indicated on the motor nameplate, secure the compressor motor and wait an additional 10 minutes before starting.

i. Start the desuperheater drip at a very rapid rate.

CAUTION. Use only distilled water for the desuperheater drip.

j. Admit some water to the manometer through the fill valve at the bottom shortly after starting the compressor.

NOTE. The unit may still be taking in air through the manometer and will draw up the water. However, in a short time the water will return and the unit will stop taking air.

k. When the manometer seals, add enough water to completely fill the large outer tube. The water level in the outer tube will now be at zero.

NOTE. Two indications that the unit has reached the point where feed must be added are (1) a drop in the compressor pressure, and (2) an overflow of water through the overflow rotameter. The pressure drop is caused by the manometer sealing itself and stopping the compressor from drawing in air. The overflow is caused by the boiling over of water from the steam chest. This overflow will stop as soon as the excess water has boiled over.

l. Set the compressor speed at approximately 2,000 rpm. Note the ammeter while adjusting the compressor speed. Do not exceed 1.2 times the rated motor amperes as indicated on the motor nameplate. If a tachometer is not available, adjust the motor speed to produce 45- to 50-gph condensate rate.

m. When the manometer reads plus 2 inches (the level in the inside tube 2 inches above the level in the outer tube), start the feed pump and adjust the flow control valve to give a 5-gph flow in the feed rotameter.

n. When the manometer reads plus 4 inches, set the feed rate at 10 gph.

NOTE. When the manometer does not rise to a plus 4 inches reading with this feed rate, or if the manometer goes up very slowly, trouble or unusual conditions are indicated. Read the instructions for starting the unit with low voltage or low compressor speed and proceed accordingly. See Section 8E3.

o. When the manometer reads plus 6 inches, set the feed rate at 15 gph.

NOTE. If, in actual operation, the manometer overflows when the above rates of feed are added it may be necessary to increase the amounts to as much as 10, 20, and 30 gph when the manometer reads plus 2, 4, and 6.

p. When the manometer level starts to go above a plus 6 inches reading with a 15-gph feed rate, vent the steam trap and start closing the bypass valve slowly, keeping the manometer above plus 3 inches and keeping the compressor discharge pressure below 6 pounds.

q. When the bypass valve is entirely closed, increase the feed rate 10 to 20 gph at intervals not to exceed 30 seconds as indicated by the manometer level, until the feed rate is about 70 gph.

The unit is now operating and making condensate, but it will require a slight adjustment of the feed rate during the next 2 hours to achieve a balance. The balance will be indicated by the pressure level in the manometer.

NOTE. Do not increase the feed rate when the manometer is on the minus side or falling.

r. Balance the unit by adjusting the flow control valve to obtain about 70-gph minimum feed rate, and use enough electric heaters so that the manometer will balance and remain constant at a point between plus 2 inches and minus 4 inches.

s. Adjust the desuperheater drip to give a minimum compressor pressure. Increasing the number of drops per minute lowers the pressure up to a certain point where a further increase in the desuperheater drip will cause the pressure to increase. The desuperheater drip should be kept adjusted to give this low point of compressor pressure. As the evaporator scales up, a faster drip rate will be required. A dirty evaporator will require a small steady stream in the drip sight glass.

t. Operating details:

To increase the overflow—increase the feed.

To decrease overflow—decrease the feed.

To make the manometer rise—turn on the electric heaters or reduce the feed rate.

To make the manometer fall—increase the feed rate or turn off the electric heaters.

To increase the condensate rate—increase the compressor speed.

To reduce the condensate rate—reduce the compressor speed.

CAUTION. The maximum compressor speed is limited only by the allowable motor overload. The normal speed is 2,000 rpm, and this is the preferred speed since it is the rated rpm for the installation. Conditions may arise when it may be necessary to increase or reduce the condensate rate by varying the compressor speed. Keep the desuperheater drip adjusted to give a minimum compressor pressure. In a heavy sea or when the voltage is fluctuating, operate the unit to balance the manometer between plus 2 inches and plus 4 inches.

CAUTION. Should the unit lose heat and take in air through the manometer, open the bypass valve immediately and proceed from Step n to restart the unit.

8B2. Watch readings and log. The following are the recommended hourly watch readings: time; hours run since last cleaning; compressor pressure; compressor rpm; feed rate; overflow rate; gallons of condensate distilled; feed pressure; manometer reading; number of heaters on; volts; amperes; condensate salinity; fill desuperheater tank; time distillation started; and time unit secured.

Record the data from the first run of the new unit or units under the headings given above.

A log book should be kept on the distilling unit and the above data recorded at least every 50 hours. It should also be recorded just prior to and immediately after every cleaning.

C. OPERATION OF THE MOTOR

8C1. Operating the motor. The feed pressure and motor speed should remain substantially constant to obtain the best operation. If the line voltage varies, the speed of the compressor and the corresponding output of the distilling unit may be somewhat increased or decreased by turning the field rheostat to change the speed of the motor.

Operation of the controller is started by pressing the start button. The motor is started through two steps of starting resistors, and acceleration is controlled by the action of series relays. The relays are adjusted to close the accelerating contactors on successive current inrushes and at 30 amperes, decreasing current. An electrical interlock on the final accelerating contactor opens the coil circuit to the first accelerating contactor which remains open during the running period.

Low voltage protection is provided, and, in the event of voltage failure, the equipment can be restarted when the voltage has been restored to the line by pressing the start button. Stopping of the motor is effected by pressing in the stop button.

The operation of the controller is subject at all times to the operation of the overload relay, which opens the circuit to the main line contactor on excessive overloads. After the overload relay has tripped, it will reset automatically, but it is necessary to press the start button to restart the motor.

Speed adjustment above or below normal is obtained by inserting a rheostat in the shunt field circuit and varying the resistance.

The operation of the motor should be continuously observed during the first few hours of operation, noting the condition of the bearings, commutator, and other parts, and observing the temperature and balance of the motor.

The heat balance of the distilling system is sensitive and all changes in the operating conditions should be made slowly.

D. STOPPING

8D1. Stopping routine.
1. Fill the desuperheater tank.
2. Turn off the electric heaters.
3. Open the bypass valve.
4. Stop the compressor motor.
5. Secure the desuperheater drip.
6. Open the flow control valve to feed 70 gph and continue feeding for 15 minutes or longer. The longer the flushing, the more effective will be the reduction of scale formation. For longer flushing, note the overflow rate and set the feed rate equal to the overflow rotameter reading.
7. Secure the flow control valve and feed pump.
8. Secure the sea chest valves.
9. Pull the main electrical switch.

CAUTION. The unit must at all times be left full of water.

E. OPERATING DIFFICULTIES

8E1. Rise of pressure in the Model X-1 unit. A clean unit will operate with a compressor discharge pressure of about 3 pounds. The compressor pressure will rise slowly as scale accumulates on the heating surfaces in the evaporator.

This rise should be about $1/10$ of a pound or less

for every 24 hours of operation. If the compressor pressure rises more rapidly than this, improper operation or trouble is indicated. If the rise is only a few tenths of a pound, it is probably due to improper operation. The hourly watch readings for the past 24 hours' operation should be checked. A feed rate below the minimum will cause the pressure to increase more rapidly. If all electric heaters are not in use and the feed rate is low, turn on additional electric heaters and increase the feed rate.

While starting the unit, the compressor pressure will be unaffected by the scale condition of the evaporator tubes. When the compressor is first started (2 hours after starting the heaters) the pressure will be about 3½ pounds with the bypass fully open. As steam is generated by the electric heaters, the pressure will slowly fall to about 1½ pounds by the time the manometer is at plus 6 inches, and it will be time to close the bypass valve (about 10 minutes after starting the compressor). As the bypass valve is closed, the compressor pressure rises. With the bypass valve fully closed the compressor pressure will be about ½ pound above the normal operating pressure existing immediately prior to the last time it was secured. (The scale condition of the tubes determines the normal operating pressure.) The compressor pressure will drop back to normal during the 30 minutes required to balance the unit after closing the bypass valve.

Operating difficulties usually encountered with this unit are discussed in Sections 8E2 through 8E8. Each section lists the difficulty, the probable causes, and the detection and remedy for each difficulty.

8E2. High compressor pressure. The probable causes of high compression pressure are *scaled tubes in the evaporator; the evaporator boiled partially dry; a condensate buildup in the steam chest* caused by the steam trap being air bound or improperly installed, the steam trap stuck closed, a plugged air vent orifice, or a restriction or closed valve in the condensate line; or *an air buildup in the steam chest* caused by a plugged, restricted, or excessively small steam chest air orifice, a restricted vent line, an air leak in the evaporator or excessive air in the feed.

The detection of each of these possible causes and the remedy for each, are as follows:

a. *Scaled tubes in evaporator.* After an extended period of operation, scale will gradually build up on the tubes. The compressor pressure should increase about 1/10 of a pound or less during 24 hours of operation due to the accumulation of scale on the inside of the tubes in the evaporator. If the compressor discharge pressure rises more rapidly than this, improper operation or trouble is indicated.

b. *Evaporator boiled partially dry.* If the level of the salt water inside the tubes is too low, heat cannot be transferred effectively and the compressor pressure rises.

Low water inside the tubes is the most frequent cause of compressor pressure going above 6 pounds when closing the bypass valve. The manometer will usually be rising rapidly and may even go over plus 10 inches. Stop closing the bypass valve at 6 pounds and increase the feed rate to 60 gph.

NOTE. If the pressure starts to fall, low water is indicated. Continue closing the bypass valve as the pressure falls and resume normal operation.

If increasing the feed rate as described above fails to cause compressor pressure to fall, the water level is not too low. Proceed as follows to determine the trouble:

c. *Condensate buildup in the steam chest.* Condensate is normally taken from the steam chest as it is formed. If the flow of condensate is restricted, it builds up in the bottom of the steam chest, blanks off part of the tubes, reduces the effective surface, and causes the compressor pressure to increase. Only a small amount of condensate is made before the bypass valve is closed. However, as soon as the bypass is completely closed, the unit is making condensate at rated capacity. Condensate buildup is the next most probable cause of a high pressure on starting.

If the condensate is building up in the evaporator, the manometer will react normally while the unit is being started until after the bypass valve is closed. From this point on, the manometer will tend to fall as the feed rate is increased and it will be impossible to bring the feed rate up even to the normal condensate rate without the manometer falling to a minus 10-inch reading and taking in air. Upon closing the bypass valve, the compressor discharge pressure will be only slightly above normal, but will increase at the rate of 3 pounds in 30 minutes. The condensate buildup will also cause a steady, small stream of water to be discharged from the open vent pipe out of the bottom of the exchanger.

Check as follows for the cause of the condensate buildup: Vent the steam trap for about a minute until water or steam appears. If steam is discharged, the condensate is probably not building up in the steam chest. Check other causes of high pressure. If water is vented from the steam trap, the condensate may be building up in the steam chest. Check the condensate rate by breaking the line to test tanks or by opening the sample cock on the cold side of the heat exchanger. If the condensate rate is low or zero for the given compressor speed, something is wrong with the mechanism of the steam trap. Secure the unit and inspect the mechanism steam trap. Check to see that the condensate line is open and not restricted.

d. *Air buildup in the steam chest.* The steam chest air vent orifice is of such size ($\frac{3}{64}$-inch for X-1 units) that all of the air normally dissolved in the sea water will be continually vented from the steam chest. Accumulation of air in the steam chest will blank off some of the tubes, reduce the effective surface, and cause the compressor discharge pressure to increase.

e. *Plugged, restricted, or too small steam chest air vent orifice or a restricted vent line.* If the vent orifice or vent line is entirely plugged or restricted, the manometer will tend to seal a little sooner than normal, but will react entirely normally from that point on. The compressor discharge pressure will be substantially above normal as soon as the bypass valve is closed. The unit will otherwise be normal in appearance and operation with the exception of the compressor discharge which will continue to rise at about the rate of 2 pounds in 30 minutes after the bypass valve is closed. If the vent orifice is only partially plugged or too small, the compressor discharge pressure will not rise so fast and may stop rising. The unit will operate normally except that a higher pressure may exist than the scale or compressor speed will indicate. Place a cup of water over the open end of the vent pipe at the bottom of the heat exchanger and look for air bubbles. Air bubbles indicate that the vent line or orifice is not entirely plugged. If entirely plugged, check the valves in the vent line. Secure the unit and inspect the vent orifice.

f. *Air leak into the evaporator.* When the unit is operating with the manometer on the minus side, any leak in the atmospheric pressure or compressor suction part of the evaporator will let air into the unit. The steam chest orifice will not vent this extra air and the compressor discharge pressure increases proportionally to the amount of air leakage. If the manometer is on the plus side, no air can leak into the unit; instead, steam will leak out.

If an air leak is suspected, start the unit in the usual manner, keeping the manometer always on the plus side. After the unit is in operation, test for an air leak as follows: Balance the unit with the manometer at about plus 4 inches and note the compressor discharge pressure. Increase the feed or secure heaters to balance the unit with a minus 6-inch to 8-inch manometer reading. Note the compressor discharge pressure. Balance the unit with the manometer at about plus 4 inches and note the compressor discharge pressure. If the compressor discharge pressure rises with a minus manometer, but returns to normal with a plus manometer, the unit has an air leak. Operate the unit with the manometer at about plus 4 inches or 6 inches and look at the following points for leakage of steam:

1. Loose glass in sight drip valve.

2. Loose connection between the drip valve and compressor.

3. Drip valve open and desuperheater tank dry.

4. Loose packing nut or worn rubber washers in the manometer.

5. Leak in the bypass valve packing nut.

6. The check valve after the manometer may be stuck open or worn out.

7. Loose packing glands on compressor.

Loose compressor glands usually leak steam even with minus manometer, but may possibly let air leak in on a few compressors.

8. Gasket joints leaking at:
   (a) manhole cover
   (b) top joint of evaporator shell
   (c) bypass valve flange
   (d) center joint of evaporator shell
   (e) compressor base
   (f) compressor top

g. *Excessive air in feed.* Check the feed rotameter for large bubbles of air. As soon as the air is eliminated from the feed the compressor pressure will return to normal.

8E3. Minimum feed rate and manometer sealing difficulty. Sometimes the unit while in operation does not take the minimum feed rate specified without the manometer falling to minus 10 inches, or while starting, the manometer takes unusually long to seal and rises very slowly or not at all, even with a small flow of feed. These difficulties are probably caused by *too large a steam chest orifice; a steam leak* at the *compressor glands or elsewhere; low compressor speed; low heater volts or burned out heaters;* or *the steam trap being stuck open.*

The detection of these possible causes and the remedy for each, are as follows:

When the feed rate to balance the unit (a manometer reading between plus 2 inches and minus 4 inches) with all the electric heaters on, is below the minimum feed rate specified, the heat losses are excessive or the energy input insufficient.

a. *Steam leak at the compressor glands or elsewhere.* The usual source of excessive heat losses is a steam leak at the compressor glands or elsewhere. Even a small steam leak can cause a high loss of heat and must be corrected. The following conditions will give an insufficient energy input:

1. Burned out or shorted electric heaters or a blown heater fuse. To determine while operating the unit whether an electric heater is defective, turn each switch off, then on. Note the change in the ammeter reading. Fix or replace the heater at once.

2. On installations (submarines particularly) where the back pressure on the condensate is low, a stuck open steam trap will cause excessive heat loss and the manometer will be very erratic. Starting will be very difficult.

b. *Low compressor speed or low heater voltage.* With a scaled evaporator, the compressor pressure will be high, so that the unit will operate satisfactorily at low compressor speeds or with low heater voltage. A clean unit has the minimum compressor pressure and energy input. With a low compressor speed or low heater voltage, it may be impossible to maintain the minimum feed rate specified. Of course, if compressor speed is low the condensate rate will be low and the minimum feed rate required is 1.4 times the actual condensate rate. If the heater voltage is low and it is impossible to increase it, the unit may be operated at a reduced feed rate until sufficient scale

has been formed in the evaporator. This will increase the energy input to the compressor and allow the minimum feed rate to be maintained. Operation at a feed rate below 1.4 times the condensate rate should be kept to a minimum and avoided if at all possible.

When the manometer takes unusually long to seal or will not rise readily to plus 6 inches with the feed rates as specified in starting Steps m, n, and o, under Section 8B1, check for excessive heat loss in the manner described above. Inspect the steam chest air vent orifice and check the compressor speed and heater voltage. Correct the excessive loss if any, or proceed as follows to start the unit if the manometer continues to rise slowly.

c. *Starting procedure for low compressor speed or low heater voltage.*

1. Turn on the main electrical switch.

2. Line up the valves in the feed, condensate, brine overflow and vent lines.

3. Start the feed pump. Check the feed pressure gage, venting the feed pump if necessary. The minimum feed pressure is 25 pounds.

4. Open the feed flow control valve and observe the flow in the feed rotameter; adjust the feed so as to have a flow of 90 gph.

5. When the flow begins in the brine overflow rotameter, secure the flow control valve and the feed pump.

6. Turn on the electric heater switches, checking the ammeter as each switch is turned on.

CAUTION. The electric heaters burn out unless covered with water. Do not turn on the electric heaters without first filling the unit with water, as evidenced by a flow in the brine overflow rotameter.

7. Check the following in preparation for starting the compressor motor:

Bypass valve. The bypass valve must always be fully open when the compressor is started.

Belts. Belts must have slack. Belts that are too tight will cause the compressor to bind and will overload the motor.

Desuperheater water. Check the water level in the tank. The tank should be at least half full.

Oil levels in compressor. Compressor oil levels must be midway in the sight glasses when the ship is on an even keel and the compressor is not running.

CAUTION. Use only Navy No. 9370 or SAE 40 oil in the compressor.

Rheostat. Motors must always be started at the lowest speed with the rheostat all the way to the left.

8. Start the compressor motor 2 hours after turning on the electric heaters.

CAUTION. Check motor ampere reading. If it is greater than 1.2 times the rated motor current as indicated on the motor nameplate, secure the compressor motor and wait an additional 10 minutes before starting.

9. Start the desuperheater drip at a very rapid rate.

CAUTION. Use only distilled water for the desuperheater drip.

10. Admit some water to the manometer through the fill valve at the bottom shortly after starting the compressor.

NOTE. The unit may still be taking in air through the manometer and will draw up the water. However, in a short time the water will return and the unit will stop taking air.

11. When the manometer seals, add enough water to completely fill the large outer tube. The water level in the outer tube will now be at zero.

NOTE. Two indications that the unit has reached the point where feed must be added are: (1) a drop in the compressor pressure, and (2) an overflow of water through the overflow rotameter. The pressure drop is caused by the manometer sealing itself and stopping the compressor from drawing in air. The overflow is caused by the boiling over of water from the steam chest. This overflow will stop as soon as the excess water has boiled over.

12. When the manometer reads plus 2 inches, start the feed pump and open the feed valve to give 5 to 8 gph or less flow in the feed rotameter.

13. When the manometer reads plus 5 inches, vent the steam trap and start closing the bypass valve, keeping the manometer above minus 2 inches and the compressor pressure below 6 pounds.

14. As soon as the bypass valve is entirely closed, start increasing the feed rate 5 to 10 gph every half minute or less, as indicated by the manometer level, until the feed rate is about 60 gph.

15. Determine the condensate rate, if at low compressor speed, and maintain the minimum feed rate of 1.4 times the condensate rate.

16. Proceed to balance the unit as described in Step p under Section 8B1. For the first 3 or 4 hours of operation of a new or clean unit, at low compressor speed or heater voltage, it will probably be impossible to maintain the feed rate above 60 gph.

8E4. Low flow in feed rotameter. Sometimes with the flow control valve fully open and the feed pump running, the flow in the feed rotameter is low. Some of the possible causes of this difficulty are an *air bound feed pump; dirty strainers on the feed pump discharge; clogged strainer on the feed pump suction; clogged or dirty flow control valve; dirty heat exchanger or scaled feed piping between the exchanger and the evaporator; or a nonfunctioning water regulating valve.*

The detection of these possible causes and the remedy for each, are as follows:

a. *Feed pump air bound.* Open the vent valve on the feed pump and be certain that all the air is expelled.

b. *Dirty strainers on the feed pump discharge.* One strainer should be used at a time. Change to the second strainer, remove the cap on the first strainer and clean the screen.

c. *Clogged Macomb type strainer on suction.* Examine the strainer on the suction to the feed pump and clean it if necessary. Be sure to vent all air from this strainer.

d. *Flow control valve clogged or dirty.* Remove the valve bonnet and examine the valve. Clean if necessary.

e. *Dirty heat exchanger.* The heat exchanger tubes and piping between exchanger and evaporator will gradually become scaled. When the scale deposit is too great, the flow to the unit will be restricted. When this condition is reached, remove the end covers and follow the cleaning instructions.

f. *Water regulating valve not functioning.* Remove the cap on the top of the valve and clean out the valve. Flush water through the valve with the cap out. Replace the cap and operate the valve. If the valve cannot be made to function, remove it from the line and connect the feed pump directly to the flow control valve, regulating the feed to the unit by hand. Have the water regulating valve overhauled at a naval shipyard or tender.

8E5. Low flow in brine overflow rotameter. The probable causes of this low flow are a *closed valve in the overflow line; a scaled overflow pipe; or a dirty heat exchanger.*

The detection of these possible causes and the remedy for each, are as follows:

a. *Valve closed in overflow line.* Check all valves in the overflow line, making certain that they are open.

b. *Overflow pipe scaled.* After an extended period of operation, the overflow pipe from the evaporator to the brine overflow pump and heat exchanger becomes scaled. Disassemble this pipe and clean it according to the instructions given.

8E6. Salt in condensate. Salt may accumulate in the condensate because of a *salt leak in the exchanger; worn fiber bushings on the exchanger tubes or a salt leak in the exchanger;* or because of a *salt leak in the evaporator* caused by too high a water level in the evaporator, a restriction in the vent line or a tube leak in the evaporator.

The detection of these possible causes and the remedy for each, are as follows:

When the condensate in the test tanks shows salt, check the salinity of the condensate between the evaporator and the exchanger and check the salinity of the water in the desuperheater tank. If the desuperheater tank has high salinity, secure the drip to the compressor and check the salinity of the condensate before and after the exchanger every 5 minutes.

a. *Salt leak in exchanger and worn fiber bushings.* With no desuperheater drip, the salinity of the condensate should be satisfactory before the exchanger but should be high after the exchanger. Secure the unit, remove the covers on the exchanger, and look for leaks around the tubes and bushings. The exchanger is full of condensate and any leak usually shows up as soon as the covers are removed. However, if no leaks show up, place small pipe sleeves over the studs and tighten the units securely. Put 10 to 15 pounds of air or water pressure on the condensate, and check the tubes and bushings again for leaks. Replace any leaky tubes using new fiber and metallic bushings. If a bushing leaks, remove the bushings from the lower three rows of the exchanger tubes and repack with new fiber and metallic bushings. It is not improbable that the unit will make distilled water even though the fiber bushing has worn out. In this case, the condensate is leaking into the feed. Check the condensate rate, and check the salinity of the condensate drawn from the exchanger while the unit is not running. If a bushing has gone, the

condensate rate will be low and will be salty when the unit first starts distilling.

IMPORTANT. Experience shows that the bushings on the hot feed and brine tubes will wear out after about 1,500 to 2,000 hours' operation. Replace fiber and metallic bushings on the lower four rows of the feed and overflow tubes after every 1,500 hours of operation on the heat exchanger. Completely repack the entire exchanger (feed, ¾-inch tubes, and condensate, 1¼-inch tubes) after every 3,000 hours of operation on the heat exchanger.

b. *Salt leak in evaporator.* 1. *The water level may be too high* in the evaporator because of a restricted overflow line on surface craft, or a restricted safety overflow vent line on submarines. If the overflow line becomes restricted, sea water will build up in the evaporator. When the level approaches the vapor separator baffles, excessive entrainment will be carried over and will cause the condensate to be salty. The flow out of the vent from the exchanger will be a steady stream. Also, the overflow rotameter will read lower than normally for a given feed rate. If the safety overflow line on submarines is kept open, a sea water buildup in the evaporator is impossible.

2. *Restriction in vent line.* If the vent line is restricted or has a seal, entrainment will not be vented from the vapor separator and may build-up, causing salt to be carried over into the condensate. Check the vent line for a seal or restrictions.

3. *Tube leak in evaporator.* If the leak is only a small one, the unit will probably make good condensate, but salt water will leak into the steam chest when the unit is not in operation. If the leak is a large one, the condensate will be salty during operation. Remove the manhole cover, fill the evaporator to the level of the funnel, and start the compressor. Close the bypass valve to obtain a 5-pound discharge pressure and look for air bubbles. Replace or reroll the leaky tube.

8E7. Noisy compressor. A noisy compressor may be caused by *insufficient or too low viscosity oil; tight belts; or worn gears or bushings.*

The detection of these possible causes and the remedy for each, are as follows:

a. *Insufficient or too low viscosity oil.* Check the level of oil in the oil sight glasses when the compressor is not running and add sufficient oil to show about halfway in the glasses. Use only Navy Symbol 1150 or SAE 70 oil in Roots-Connersville compressors. Use only SAE 40 or Navy Symbol 9370 oil in General Motors compressors. *Lower viscosity* oil than specified will hasten the wearing of the gears.

b. *Tight belts.* The belts between the motor and the compressor must be adjusted so that the belts will bow out about an inch when the compressor is running. Belts that are too tight will cause the compressor to bind. Adjustment may be made with the variable pitch drive on the motor.

c. *Worn gears or bearings.* Worn gears or bearings should be replaced by a naval shipyard or tender.

8E8. Excessive compressor motor current. This high current may be caused by *belts that are too tight, compressor packing that is too tight,* or by *a worn compressor.*

The detection of these possible causes and the remedy for each, are as follows:

a. *Too-tight belts.* Adjust the belts with variable pitch drive so that the belts will bow about an inch on the slack side during operation.

b. *Compressor packing too tight.* Loosen the packing gland and allow the compressor to operate until the steam blows out of each gland. Tighten the glands evenly and only to a point where steam does not leak.

c. *Worn compressor.* Have the compressor changed as soon as possible.

8E9. Low feed rate. Sometimes the feed rate to the balance unit is below the minimum when all

the electric heaters are being used. This condition may be caused by *a steam trap being stuck open, a dirty heat exchanger, leaky compressor packing glands, electric heaters not all operating,* or *insufficient compressor speed.*

The detection of these possible causes and the remedy for each, are as follows:

a. *Steam trap stuck open.* Shut down the unit, remove the flanged cover on the trap, and check to see that the mechanism moves freely.

b. *Dirty heat exchanger.* Clean the heat exchanger as directed in the section on cleaning.

c. *Leaky compressor packing glands.* Tighten the packing glands carefully until no steam leaks. Pull down slowly until steam just stops leaking, otherwise the packing will be too tight. Change the packing when necessary.

d. *Electric heaters not all operating.* The operation of the electric heaters may be noted by snapping the heater switches on and off, one at a time, and observing the ammeter readings. If the ammeter readings do not change in accordance with the heater requirements when operating a particular switch, a fuse may be out, the wiring require testing, or a heater must be changed.

e. *Insufficient compressor speed.* On d. c. units, speed up the compressor with the field rheostat. On a. c. units expand the variable pitch drive as much as possible on the motor without having the belts too tight. If the compressor speed is still too low, follow the operating instructions for low compressor speed.

F. DISTILLING UNITS WITH SNORKEL CONVERSIONS OPERATING INSTRUCTIONS

8F1. These instructions and starting procedures approximate the procedures outlined for the Model X-1 (AAA-1) before their conversion.

STARTING:

IMPORTANT: Before starting unit, pump bilges so that hot pipes connecting heat exchanger and evaporator are not submerged. During operation keep bilge low enough to keep these lines out of the water.

1. Turn on the main electrical switch.

2. Check the valves in the feed line so that there will be an unrestricted flow of water.

3. Start the feed pump. Check the feed pressure gage, venting the feed pump if necessary.

4. Open the feed flow-control valve and observe the flow in the feed rotameter.

5. Check the valves in the brine overflow line so that there will be an unrestricted flow of water and observe the brine overflow rotameter.

6. Vent overflow lines at high points for entrapped air. If during operation with a feed rate below 90 gph overflow comes out safety vent, vent high points on overflow line. When the flow begins in the brine overflow rotameter, secure the flow control valve and the feed pump. (*UNIT IS NOW FILLED WITH WATER.*)

7. Turn on all manual and automatic control electric heater switches, checking ammeter as each switch is turned on.

CAUTION. The electric heaters will burn out unless covered with water. Do not turn on electric heaters without first filling the unit with water as evidenced by a flow in the brine overflow rotameter.

8. Check the valves in the condensate line so that there will be an unrestricted flow of water.

9. Check the following in preparation to starting the compressor motor:

a. *Bypass valve.* The bypass valve must be fully open when the compressor is started.

b. *Belts.* Belts must have slack. Excessively tight belts will cause the compressor to bind and will overload the motor.

c. *Oil level in compressor.* Compressor oil levels must be midway in the glasses when the ship is on an even keel and the compressor is not running.

CAUTION. Use only Navy Symbol 9370 or SAE 40 oil in the compressor.

d. *Rheostat.* Motors must always be started at the lowest speed with the rheostat all the way to the left.

10. Start the compressor motor when pressure switches cut out the automatic heaters about one and one-half hours after turning on the electric heaters.

CAUTION. Check compressor motor amperage. If more than 1.2 times rated motor current as shown on the motor nameplate, secure motor and wait an additional 10 minutes before starting. Allowance must be made for the current drawn by the heaters.

11. Start the desuperheater drip at a very rapid rate.

CAUTION. Use only distilled water for the desuperheater drip.

12. Set the compressor speed at about 2,000 rpm. Note the ammeter while adjusting the compressor speed. Do not increase speed so that ammeter reading of motor current will exceed 1.2 times rated motor current as shown on motor nameplate. If tachometer is not available adjust compressor speed to give about 45 gph of condensate.

13. When the gage shows between 2 inches and 4 inches pressure, start the feed pump and adjust flow control valve to give 5 gph flow in the feed rotameter.

14. When the gage reading reaches 4 inches pressure set the feed rate at 10 gph. IMPOR-

TANT: If gage will not rise to 4 inches reading with 5 gph, feed rate, or rises slowly, trouble or unusual conditions are indicated. Read instructions for starting unit with low voltage or low compressor speed and proceed accordingly. Section 8F2.

15. When gage reaches 6 inches pressure, increase the feed rate to 15 gph.

16. As the pressure starts to go above 6 inches with a feed rate of 15 gph, start closing the bypass valve slowly, keeping the gage reading on the pressure side and the compressor discharge pressure below 6 pounds.

17. When the bypass valve is entirely closed, increase the feed rate by 15 to 20 gph at intervals not to exceed 30 seconds, until the feed rate is about 70 gph (see note). The unit is now operating and making condensate, but will require a slight adjustment of the feed rate during the next 30 minutes to balance the unit as indicated by the gage.

NOTE. *DO NOT INCREASE FEED RATE WHEN THE GAGE READS ON THE VACUUM SIDE AND FALLING.*

18. Balance the unit by adjusting the flow-control valve for a 70 gph minimum feed rate. Then, depending on feed water temperature keep as many heaters going as is necessary to hold the gage reading between 6 inches and 12 inches pressure.

(NOTE. For full operating efficiency during high voltage of battery charge, increase feed slightly. This will also tend to keep compressor pressure normal.)

Under most conditions, the two switches (four heaters) that operate automatically will be sufficient to maintain this pressure. However, if feed water is very warm, only one switch (two heaters) in automatic operation might be necessary, or if feed water is extremely cold, the manual switched heaters on continuously, might be necessary to maintain the 6 inches to 12 inches pressure reading.

19. Adjust the desuperheater drip to give a minimum compressor pressure.

20. OPERATING DETAILS.

To increase overflow—increase feed.

To decrease overflow—decrease feed.

To make gage pressure rise—turn on electric heaters or reduce feed.

To make gage pressure fall—turn off electric heaters or increase feed.

To increase condensate rate—increase compressor speed.

To reduce condensate rate—decrease compressor speed.

CAUTION. Maximum speed of compressor is limited only by allowable motor overload. At no time increase compressor speed overload to more than 1.2 times the rated amperage. Keep the desuperheater drip adjusted to give a minimum compressor pressure. In a heavy sea, or when voltage is fluctuating because of high speed operations on battery, operate the unit to balance the gage pressure at 6 inches to 12 inches.

CAUTION. Should the unit lose heat and the gage indicate a vacuum, open the bypass valve immediately and proceed from step 15 to restart unit.

8F2. Starting procedures for low compressor speed or low heater voltage.

Follow starting procedure, steps 1 through 12, and proceed as follows for steps 13 through 17.

13. When gage reads 2 inches pressure, start feed pump and open feed valve to give 5 to 8 gph in feed rotameter.

14. When gage reads 5 inches pressure, vent steam trap. Start closing bypass, keeping gage reading above 2 inches vacuum.

15. When bypass valve is entirely closed, increase feed rate by 5 to 10 gph about every 30 seconds, until feed rate is about 60 gph. (See note below.)

The unit is now operating and making condensate.

NOTE. Do not increase feed rate when gage indicates a vacuum and falling.

16. Determine condensate rate, if compressor speed is low, and maintain minimum feed rate of 1.4 times condensate rate.

17. Proceed to balance units as from step 18. For the first three or four hours operations of a new or clean unit at low compressor speed or heater voltage it will probably be impossible to maintain feed rate above 60 gph.

9

CARE AND MAINTENANCE
OF THE MODEL X–1 DISTILLING UNIT

A. REPAIRS

9A1. Evaporator. Repairs to the shell sections and the head of the evaporator can be made only at locations where careful preheating can be done before brazing, and where facilities for annealing the entire section at about 750° F. after brazing are available. Small cracks in a seam however, may be repaired by carefully heating and then covering the crack with soft solder.

Leaky tubes may be rolled with the expanders provided in the spare parts box, or the tubes may be driven out and replaced in the usual manner.

9A2. Heat exchanger. The heat exchanger is of special type construction with the tubes made tight by packing rings. The packing rings are of both metallic and fiber construction and the exchanger may leak a little if it has been standing a long time without use or if it has just been repaired with new packing. When this occurs the exchanger tubes should be filled with water and allowed to stand for 3 or 4 hours during which time the fiber material will swell and the exchanger will then be tight under test. The exchanger should not leak in service since the packing will always be wet.

9A3. Procedure for packing exchanger. The packing for the exchanger is shipped in packages, each package containing 120 each of the fiber and metallic rings for the 1¼-inch i. d. tubes and 120 each of the fiber and metallic rings for the ¾-inch o. d. finned or wired tubes. Always use a fiber ring first and a metallic ring second when packing ¾-inch tubes, and a metallic ring first and a fiber ring second when packing 1¼-inch tubes. Packing tools will be found in the spare parts boxes.

It will normally never be necessary to replace the 1¼-inch tubes, but should this have to be done, all the ¾-inch tubes must be driven out and the plates removed before work may be done on the 1¼-inch tubes. The ¾-inch tubes are easily removed so that the 1¼-inch tubes may be exposed in a relatively short period of time. Care should be taken in selecting the proper size metallic and fiber packing for each tube because the sizes are only slightly different.

To repack the ¾-inch tubes proceed as follows:

a. Remove the nuts and covers from both ends of the exchanger.

b. Place the pipe sleeves over the studs and replace the nuts to hold the plates together.

c. Secure the guide pin tool for the ¾-inch wired or finned tubes from the spare parts box. This is piece No. 811–1c.

d. Insert the guide pin tool in the ¾-inch tube and drive the tube just through the plate, using the wooden mallet.

e. Drive out the ¾-inch tubes which need repacking.

f. Remove the old packing rings, being careful not to scratch or score the packing box.

g. Remove all the packing rings from the drillings.

h. On the opposite end of the exchanger, push the tubes back into the tube sheet and drive through as in Step d. Remove the old packing rings as described in Steps f and g.

i. Place the tubes back into tube sheet about flush with the face.

j. Use the packing insertion tool, piece No. 811–1a, from the spare parts box.

k. Hold the tube with the piece of wood to prevent it from coming out of the sheet while the opposite end is being packed. (It may be necessary to secure the wood in place.)

l. Insert the guide pin tool for ¾-inch tubes in the end of the tubes; place the fiber ring over the pin and press it into the tube plate, driving the packing firmly with the packing tool and a light tap of the wooden mallet or ¾-pound hammer.

m. Insert the metallic ring and drive it in the same way as a fiber ring.

n. Pack the opposite ends, using the same procedure.

o. Remove nuts and sleeves, and clean the old gasket. Use new gaskets and bolt the plates in place.

NOTE. The packing must be installed with the fiber rings in contact with the distilled water or distillate, and the metallic packing away from it.

To repack the 1¼-inch tubes proceed as follows:

a. Drive out and remove all the ¾-inch tubes and the old packing rings.

b. Block up the exchanger on wood.

c. Disconnect the pipes and remove the ¾-inch tube plates.

d. Drive in the 1¼-inch tubes so they *just clear the packing*, using the tool provided, and remove the old packing rings.

e. Drive back the 1¼-inch tubes from the opposite end to just clear the packing and remove the packing material at that end.

f. Push the tubes back flush with the tube plate; hold the opposite end of the tube and pack the same as described for ¾-inch tubes. (Insert the metallic ring first and the fiber rings second for the 1¼-inch tubes.)

g. Clean the tube plates, use new gaskets and assemble, packing the ¾-inch tubes as previously described.

9A4. The vapor compressor.

When a complete overhaul of the compressor is necessary, it must be removed from the distilling plant. Remove the belt guard, loosen the variable pitch drive and take off the belts. Disconnect the motor leads and take out the bolts holding the motor to the motor support on top of the compressor. Remove the motor from the compressor. Remove the insulating board. Remove the compressor lagging and take off all the oil piping after draining the oil from the compressor. Remove the pressure gage and piping where needed. It is advisable to mark the oil piping so that it may be put back in the exact location. Take off all the nuts and lockwashers, attaching the compressor to the distilling unit, and break the gasketed joint, using jack bolts if available, and lift off the compressor.

NOTE. It is very desirable that any repairs to a vapor compressor be done by a tender or a naval shipyard.

9A5. Disassembly.

(See Figure 9–1.) Rer the motor supporting plate (piece 13). Ren the cotter pin (piece 28), the nut (piece 27) washer (piece 26), and remove the pulley (p 83) using the puller. Remove the drive end c (piece 14). Remove the gear housing (piece. Remove the cotter pins from the shaft nuts (p 77), and remove the nuts. Remove the b (pieces 64 and 70), the dowel retainer and do from driven gear (piece 19) and remove the g from the hub. Remove the bearing locki (piece 42) and the lockwashers (piece 44) fi the rotor shafts. Using the gear puller provi in the spare parts box, remove the driven gear l (piece 20) and the drive gear (piece 18) from shafts and remove the keys.

NOTE. The driven gear must be loosened fr the hub and removed first before atempting remove the drive gear. If this is not done, rotors will be damaged.

Match mark the bearing retainers with the (plates so that the parts may be reassembled in same relationship. Remove the bolts (piece t from the bearing retainer plate (piece 46) a by using the puller, pull out bearing retain (piece 32). This will also bring out the bearir and oil slingers. Remove the shims (piece 4 carefully noting their number and position so tl they may be reinstalled correctly.

On the drive end of the compressor, remove t bearing locknuts and lockwashers (pieces 42 a 44). Remove the oil slinger and spacer (piece 4 from the driven shaft. Remove the bolts (pie 63) from the bearing retainers (piece 32). I means of the puller, the bearing retainers wi bearings and oil slingers may be pulled out. R move the packing glands (piece 53) from tl shafts. Remove the shaft sleeves (pieces 36 ai 37).

Match mark the end plates with the cylind so that the parts may be reassembled in the san relationship. Remove the bolts and lockwashe (pieces 61, 80, and 75) that hold the drive en plate (piece 10) to the cylinder. Remove tl end plate from the cylinder. The dowels (pie 81) that position the end plate to the cylinde should remain in the cylinder. The end plat at the gear end of the compressor (piece 10 may be removed in the same manner after th

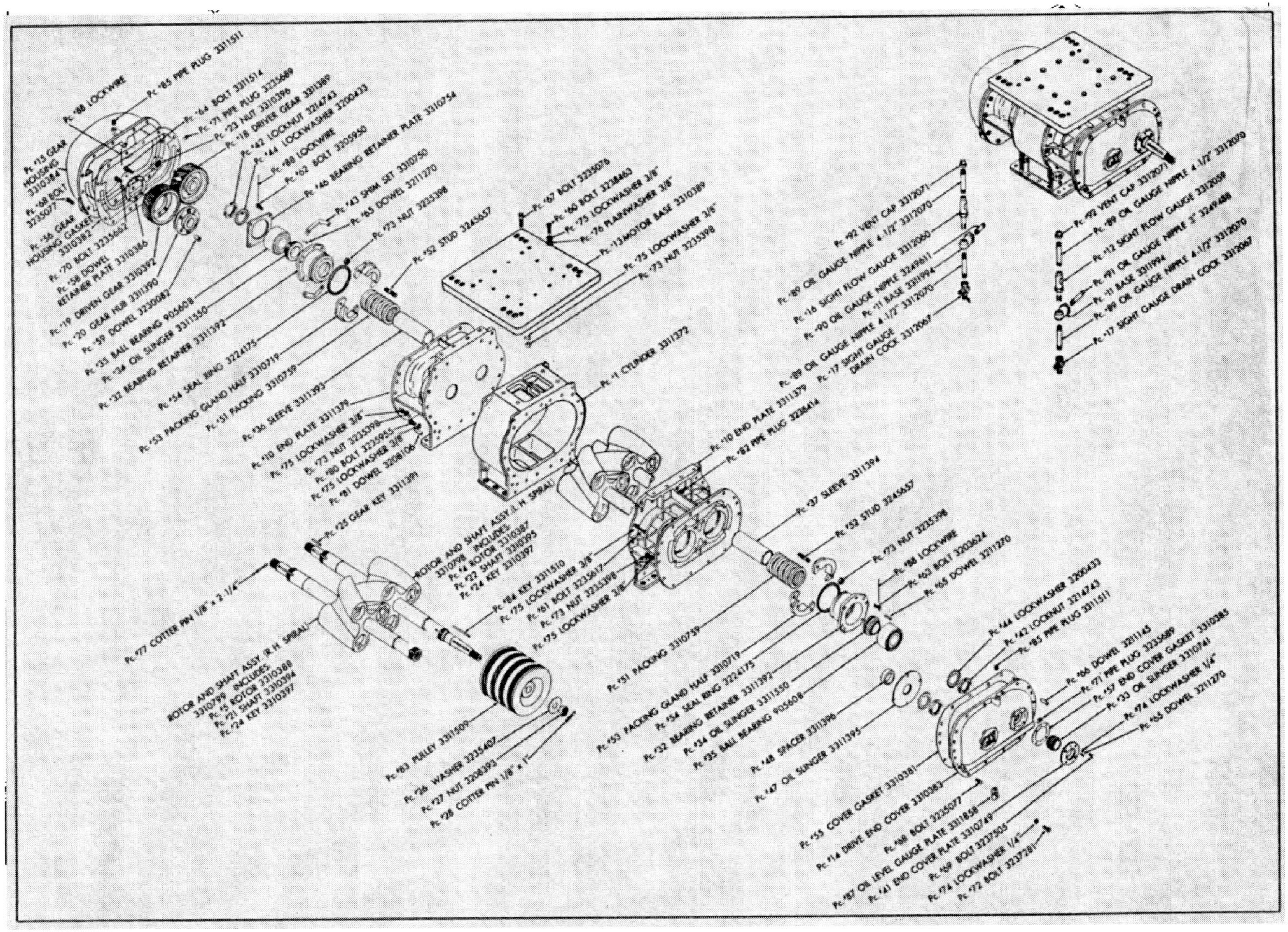

Figure 9-1. Vapor compressor, three lobe (exploded view).

iafts and rotors have been removed. Remove
ie packing (piece 51) from the end plates.

A6. Assembly. (See Figure 9-1.) Before as-
mbling the compressor, all parts should be
oroughly cleaned and inspected. Any slight
irrs or rough edges on the cylinder or end plates
ould be removed with crocus cloth. Install the
iaft sleeves (pieces 36 and 37), packing (piece
l), and packing glands (piece 53) in both end
lates. The sleeves for the gear end (piece 36)
ive a smaller inside diameter than the sleeves
ir the drive end (piece 37).

Coat the face of the gear end plate (piece 10)
id the cylinder (piece 1) with Perfect Seal No.
. manufactured by the P. O. B. Manufacturing
o., Cincinnati, Ohio, or an equivalent seal.
lace the end plate in position over the dowels
. the cylinder. Install the bolts and lockwashers
pieces 80 and 75) and tighten them evenly.
lace the cylinder upright on the end plate. In-
all the drive shaft and rotor into the cylinder
ith the gear end down. Turn the keyway in
ie shaft to the left (looking at the top of the
impressor). Install the driven shift and rotor
:to the cylinder, gear end down and keyway
. the shaft to the left (looking at the top of the
impressor).

NOTE. The drive shaft is on the right when
sembling the compressor in this manner. The
iyways in both shafts must be to the left or to
ie right (looking at the top of the compressor).

Coat the faces of the drive end plate (piece 10)
id the cylinder with Perfect Seal No. 4 or equiv-
ent. Install the drive end plate over the shafts
id over the dowels in the cylinder. Install the
lts and lockwashers (pieces 80 and 75) and
ghten evenly. Install the bearing retainers
iece 32) with the oil slingers (piece 34) and
arings (piece 35). Make certain that the oil
als (piece 54) are in place in the grooves in
e retainers. It will be necessary to press the
arings on to the shafts by using special tools.
ake certain that the pilot hole in the bearing
tainer lines up with the dowel in the end plate.

NOTE: If the bearings and oil slingers have
en removed from the bearing retainer, they
ould be reassembled before installing them over
e shafts. The oil slinger is installed with the
rge diameter toward the inside of the retainer

away from the bearing. The bearing is installed
with the smooth side next to the oil slinger.

Make certain that the shims (piece 43) are installed between the bearing retainers and the end
plate at the gear end of the compressor. Install
the bearing retainer plates (piece 46) at the gear
end and install and tighten the bolts. Install the
lockwashers (piece 44) and locknuts (piece 42)
in the gear end of both shafts. Tighten the locknuts and turn down the tang of the lockwashers
into the slot of the locknut.

NOTE. The gear end locknuts and bolts must
be tightened first to prevent pulling the shafts in
the rotors.

Check the rotor end clearance which should be
0.009 to 0.011 inch at each end. If necessary, add
or remove shims until the proper clearance is obtained. Install and tighten the bolts holding the
bearing retainers at the drive end. Install the
lock wire. Install the spacer (piece 48) and oil
slinger (piece 47) on the drive end of the driven
shaft. Install lockwashers (piece 44) on the drive
end of each shaft and install and tighten the locknut (piece 42). Insert the key (piece 25) in the
driven shaft (piece 21) and press the driven gear
hub (piece 20) into place. Insert the key (piece
25) in the drive shaft (piece 22) and press the
drive gear (piece 18) into place using the special
tool. With the keyways in both shafts to the right
(facing the gear end of the compressor), and with
the marked tooth space on the driven gear (piece
19) meshed with the marked tooth on the drive
gear, push the driven gear into position over the
hub using the special tool. Install the dowels
(piece 59), dowel retainer plate (piece 58) and
bolts (pieces 64 and 70). Tighten the bolts and install the lock wire. Install and tighten the shaft
nuts (piece 23) on both shafts. Insert the cutter
pins.

9A7. Clearances. Check the rotor clearances to
see that they are within the following limits:

Rotor to rotor_____ 0.014-in. to 0.018-in.
Rotor to end plate—drive
    end_____ 0.009-in. to 0.011-in.
Rotor to end plate—gear
    end_____ 0.009-in. to 0.011-in.
Rotor to cylinder_____ 0.006-in. to 0.009-in.

The rotor end clearances can be adjusted by
varying the thickness of the shims between the
bearing carrier and the end plate at the gear end.

If the rotor to rotor or rotor to cylinder clearances are incorrect, the gears and bearings should be checked for wear.

CAUTION. Do not drive against the shaft or any part mounted on the shaft after the thrust bearings (piece 35) have been clamped in place by the retainer plate (piece 46). Cover the sealing faces of the motor supporting plate (piece 13) and the cylinder with Perfect Seal No. 4 or equivalent. Install the plate on the cylinder, insert and tighten the bolts securely. Shellac a new gasket (piece 55) to the drive end cover (piece 14), grease the gasket and the face of the end plate and install the cover. Shellac a new gasket (piece 56) to the gear housing (piece 15), grease the gasket and face of the end plate and install the gear housing. Install the pulley (piece 83), washer (piece 26), and nut (piece 27) on the drive shaft. Tighten the nut and install a cotter pin (piece 28).

9A8. Mounting the compressor on the unit. Place a new gasket from the spare parts box on the top head of the distilling unit and then place the compressor over the stud bolts. Replace the lock washers and nuts and draw down the nuts uniformly. After mounting the compressor make certain that it may be easily turned by hand and that it does not bind or strike anywhere. Replace all of the oil piping around the compressor and install the lagging. Replace the insulating board. Replace the motor on top of the compressor and bolt it securely to the motor supporting plate attached to the top of the compressor. Replace the pulley on the compressor and attach the belts, tightening the belts by means of the variable pitch drive. Replace the pulley guard. Connect up the motor leads. Place the proper amount of Navy Symbol 9370 (S.A.E 40) oil in the compressor.

9A9. Preparation of the compressor for service. Start the distilling unit and observe the compressor while the unit is starting up; observe its operation carefully for a period of 2 hours after distillation has started. If the compressor shows no signs of sticking during this period, it will give satisfactory service. Should the compressor stop or bind during this operation, stop the compressor and allow it to cool until it turns freely by hand and then start the unit again.

B. CLEANING

9B1. Cleaning. At present (Jan. 1955) the acid cleaning method has almost entirely replaced the mechanical method, however, the mechanical cleaning equipment is carried on board tenders and could be used if acid cleaning equipment or material was unavailable. Both methods of cleaning are described in the following sections.

When mechanical cleaning was the only method used, the evaporator could be operated for 400 hours before cleaning. The absolute operating limit was 500 hours.

The heat exchanger was cleaned after 200 hours of operation and the operating limit was 250 hours.

Rotameters, manometers and flow-control valves were cleaned each time the evaporator was cleaned, or more often if necessary.

With the acid cleaning method, the cleaning interval is every 250 hours of operation. Less time is consumed and less work necessary to acid clean the distillers than to mechanically clean them. The heat exchanger requires cleaning at least each 250 hours of operation and, since the acid method cleans the heat exchanger, evaporator and all the connecting piping at the same time, the whole unit is cleaned with the heat exchanger.

A description of the mechanical method will be found in the following sections.

9B2. Cleaning crew. Two men comprise a cleaning crew. Unless a foot switch is provided, one man should operate the motor and one man should clean the tubes. The motor is turned on or off at the direction of the man cleaning the tubes. Make certain that the belt has sufficient slack so that it will slip if the bit becomes jammed in the tube.

9B3. Shear coupling assembly. (See Figure 9-2.) To provide protection for the small flexible shaft against excessive torque loads, a shear coupling assembly is attached to the cutter bit end of the flexible shaft. The feature of this assembly is a hexagonally shaped shear pin so constructed that it will break under excessive loads. The ends of the pin fit into hexagonally shaped housings, which in turn are enclosed in a common casing

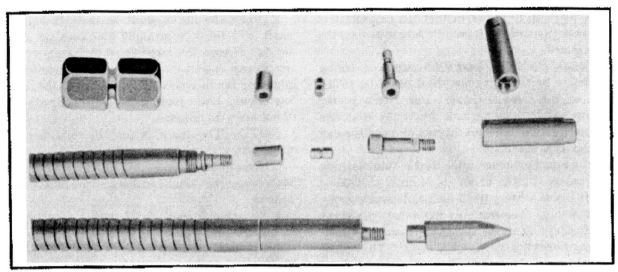

Figure 9-2. Shear coupling assembly.

which screws on to the cutter bit end of the flexible shaft casing. (This casing has a left-hand thread.) When the pin breaks, its broken ends can be easily removed from their housings and a new pin inserted.

9B4. Cleaning the evaporator. The following procedure should be observed in cleaning the evaporator:

a. Remove the section of insulation over the manhole.

b. Remove the manhole with the wrench provided in the spare parts box.

NOTE. If necessary, rig up a platform at about the level of the bottom of the evaporator.

c. Open the drain valve at the bottom and drain the evaporator (use wire if the line clogs).

d. Remove the bottom circular insulation.

e. Disconnect and remove the eight immersion heaters with the wrench from the spare parts box. Plug the heater connections with the ¾-inch pipe plugs from the tube cleaner box.

f. Clean the scale from the heaters while they are still wet.

g. Disconnect the overflow piping from the handhole at the bottom of the evaporator and plug the connection with a 1-inch or 1½-inch pipe plug from the tube cleaner box.

h. Start the feed pump. Open the feed valve and fill the evaporator so that the water level is about ⅛ inch below the tops of the tubes. Secure the feed valve and pump.

i. Place a light inside the evaporator.

j. Disconnect the feed line from the inside shell of the evaporator at the union and lift out the pipe.

k. Using the special wrench from the spare parts box, unscrew the overflow funnel pipe and remove it.

l. Chip the scale from the compressor discharge pipe and underside of the baffle. Chip the scale from the shell of the evaporator about 4 inches above the tube plate. It is advisable to cover the tube plate to prevent big chips from falling into the tubes.

m. Remove the motor and flexible shafts from the tube cleaner box and connect them as follows:

Couple the large flexible shaft and casing to the driving unit by inserting the coupling attached to the flexible shaft into the keyed hole in the countershaft spindle. Screw the casing coupling nut tightly to the threaded hub of the eccentric.

The ½-horsepower motor speed is 1,725 rpm. Lift the belt guard and place the belt on the large motor pulley, and the small countershaft pulley. This setting of the belt will produce 3,450 rpm speed at the countershaft.

NOTE. To set the speeds or adjust belt tension, pull out the small handle and turn the eccentric to loosen the belt. Place the belt on the desired pulleys, turn the eccentric in the opposite direction to tighten the belt, and replace the handle in a locking position. Do not adjust the belt tension too tightly, but allow slack so that the belt will slip in the event that the cleaning tool becomes jammed in a tube. Be sure to replace the belt guard.

Couple the 9-foot long 0.615-inch o. d. casing assembly by threading the shaft coupling to the end of the large shafting. Put grease in the bronze casing coupling, slide it over the joint, and secure the thumb nut to the section near the end of the large shaft.

The 9-foot extension cable for the tube cleaning equipment consists of an $11/_{32}$-inch o. d. flexible shaft inside a heavy 0.615-inch o. d. double interlock casing. The assembly has a hexagon shear shaft coupling in the thrust end housing of the casing assembly (cutter bit end). This shear coupling may be replaced by unscrewing the end fitting of the casing. This fitting has a *left-hand thread.* (See Figure 9–2.)

Three accessories are provided for cleaning the ¾-inch tubes, the choice of which is dictated by the nature of the deposit in the tubes. The accessories are the following:

1. *Carbide tipped cutter bit.* The cutter bit is the best and quickest method of removing hard scale formed by normal operation using untreated sea water feed. When using this bit, the tubes must be full of water. It should be used at 3,450 rpm and will clean about three tubes per minute.

2. *Expanding wire brush.* The expanding wire brush will readily remove soft scale usually formed from treated sea water feed. It will also remove hard scale if worked up and down in the tube for a long enough period. The tubes must be full of water or a stream of water must be flowing down the tubes when the expanding brush is used. It should be used at 3,450 rpm and will clean about three tubes per minute if the scale is soft. It may take 45 seconds or longer per tube if the scale is hard.

3. *Vibrating head.* The vibrating head must always be attached to a flexible holder. It will remove any type of deposit. It may be used with the tubes full of water or completely dry. It must be used when it is impossible to clean the tubes in the presence of water. The vibrating head should be used at 3,450 rpm and will take 30 seconds to 2 minutes per tube, depending on the type of scale. After using the vibrating head, the tubes must be polished with the expanding brush.

n. Place the heavy shaft so that the smaller shaft will lie in a straight line with no short bends. Grease the large cable by means of the grease cup (about 8 to 10 shots) and connect by plugging the tube cleaner motor cord to the lighting circuit. Add more grease to the large cable about every 15 minutes.

NOTE. The motor is for 110 volts d. c. on d. c. voltage vessels.

o. Examine the scale, select the proper cleaning tool from the small toolbox, and proceed as follows:

1. *Cleaning ¾-inch tubes with the cutter bit (Figure 9–3)..* The tubes must be full of water.

(a) Attach the cutter bit to the end of the small shafting.

CAUTION. The cutting edges of the tool are tipped with tungsten carbide which is quite brittle. Do not drop the bit or strike the cutting edges on metal surfaces.

(b) Start the motor and proceed to clean the tubes by passing the bit through each tube once.

NOTE. Unless a foot switch is provided, one man should operate the motor and one man should clean the tubes. The motor is turned on or off at the direction of the man cleaning the tubes.

CAUTION. With the motor off, place the end of the bit gently in the top of a tube. Hold the cable about 6 inches back and line it up exactly with the tube. Start the motor and let the bit feed itself into the tube until the entire bit is in the tube. Now exert pressure and pass the bit through the tube. (The tubes are 16–14 inches long. The fixed sleeve on the cable indicates when the bit is completely through.) Pull the bit out of the tube, stopping the motor just before the bit is withdrawn, then go on to the next one, and so forth. One bit should clean the evaporator several times. As the cutting edges become dull, more pressure will be required to force the bit through the tube. When the pressure is too great or the bit begins to jam, the cutting edges should be lightly honed. When honing is no longer possible, the cutting edges should be reground.

Should the cleaning tool fail to turn while the motor is running, the small hexagon shear coupling is probably broken. Remove the housing from the end of the casing (left-hand thread) and replace the shear coupling (Figure 9–2).

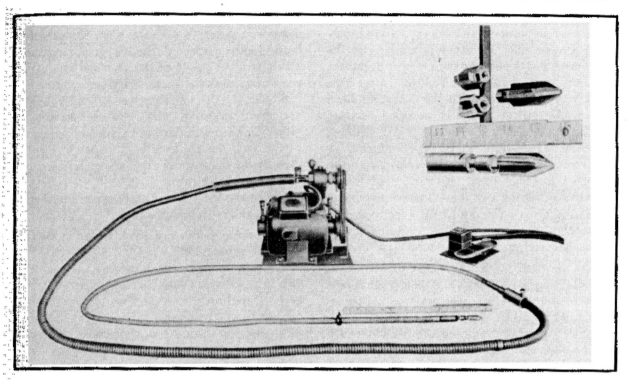

Figure 9–3. Cleaning gear with a cutter bit.

CAUTION. If the bit jams, secure the motor immediately and free the bit. Try cautiously again. If the bit continues to jam, mark the tube and go on to the next one. After the remainder of the tubes have been cleaned with the cutter bit, clean the marked tubes with the expanding brush or vibrating head, as directed in Step 2 or 3 following. The thin film of scale left by the bit in the expanded portion of the tubes will cause no trouble or loss of efficiency and need not be removed.

(c) After all the tubes have been cleaned, secure the motor, unscrew the bit (wrenches will be found in the tube cleaner box), dry, oil, and replace the bit in the box.

NOTE. If the small cable runs hot in cleaning the tubes, it should be greased. In any event, this cable should be greased at least once every hour of continual use. To grease the smaller cable, remove the flexible shafting from the inside casing and wipe with grease as it is reassembled. If the large cable runs hot, add more grease to the grease cup.

2. *Cleaning ¾-inch tubes with the expanding wire brush.* The tubes must be full of water.

(a) Attach the expanding brush to the end of the small shafting.

(b) Start the motor and work the expanding brush up and down the tube. Make certain that the brush goes entirely through each tube. The operator can tell by the vibrations of the brush when all the scale is removed. If the scale is soft it should be possible to clean two or three tubes per minute. A minute or more per tube may be required to remove the hard scale.

(c) Remove the expanding brush, dry, oil, and replace in the box.

3. *Cleaning ¾-inch tubes with the vibrating head.* The tubes may be full of water or dry.

(a) Attach the flexible holder and vibrating head to the end of the small shafting.

(b) Start the motor and work the vibrating head slowly up and down the tube. Keep the vibrating head in motion. Do not permit it to remain at one spot in the tube for any length of time. The operator can tell by the vibrations of the brush where patches of scale remain and when it has all been removed. Clean each tube completely before proceeding to the next one. A minute or more may be required per tube, depending on the hardness and type of scale.

NOTE. After using the vibrating head, the tubes must be polished with the expanding brush.

(c) Disassemble the overflow piping between the evaporator and the heat exchanger. Straight sections of 1-inch or 1½-inch I. P. S. (Iron Pipe Size) may be cleaned with the vibrating head for the 1¾-inch o. d. tubes attached directly on the small shafting (Figure 9–4). Elbows or bends in 1-inch I. P. S. pipe and sections of ¾-inch I. P. S. pipe may be cleaned with the ¾-inch vibrating head. A stream of water must be flowing through the section of pipe being cleaned, otherwise the head will become clogged with scale.

(d) Remove the vibrating head and flexible holder, dry, oil, and replace in the box.

9B5. Cleaning the 1¾-inch o. d. heater tubes and inside of overflow pipe. The scale should be removed in the presence of water (Figure 9–3).

a. Select the vibrating head and flexible holder for the 1¾-inch o. d. tubes and attach it to the end of the small shafting. Use a cleaner shaft speed of 3,450 rpm.

b. Start the motor and work the vibrating head slowly up and down the heater tubes until all the scale is removed.

NOTE. Place a clamp on the large shafting to serve as a guide to indicate when the vibrating head is entirely through the 16¼-inch long tubes.

c. Clean the inside of the overflow pipe in the same manner as the heater tubes were cleaned.

d. Remove the vibrating head, flexible holder, and small shafting. Dry, oil, and replace the vibrating head and flexible holder in the box.

e. Attach the 1¾-inch o. d. expanding brush directly to the end of the large shafting, and polish the heater tubes.

f. Remove the 1¾-inch o. d. expanding brush, dry, oil, and replace in the box.

9B6. Cleaning 4-inch o. d. tube located in the center of the evaporator.

a. Drain the water from the unit. Should the flow stop before draining is complete, insert a wire in the drain line to start the flow.

b. Connect a hose to the ship's water supply and place the end inside the evaporator. Direct a small stream of water down the sides of the 4-inch tube.

CAUTION. Do not clean the 4-inch tube when it is full of water.

c. Select the large expanding brush and attach it to the end of the large shafting.

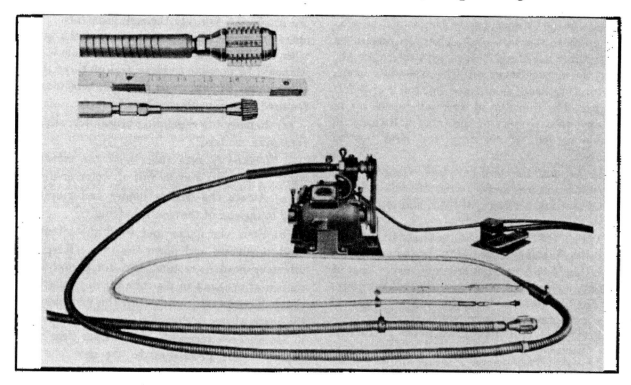

Figure 9–4. Cleaning gear with a vibrating head and expanding wire brush.

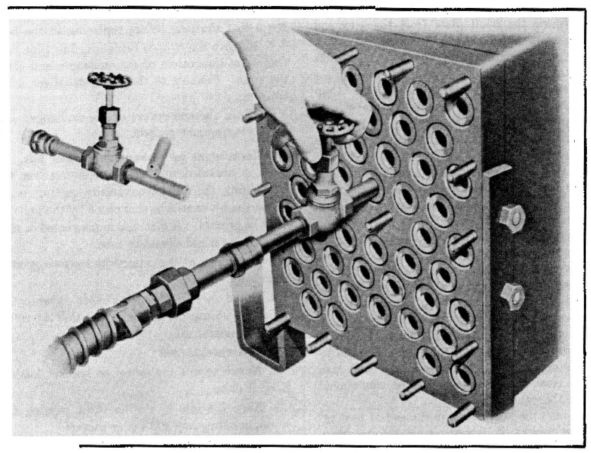

Figure 9–5. Water nozzle.

d. Remove the belt guard and place the belt on the small pulley and the large countershaft pulley to give the lowest shaft speed, approximately 1,725 rpm.

CAUTION. The 4-inch brush must be used only at *low* speed. The operator at the motor should keep his hand on the switch so that he can secure it instantly at the direction of the operator cleaning the tube.

e. Place a stop on the sleeve of the large cable so that the whole brush will not go entirely through the 16¼-inch long, 4-inch o. d. tube.

f. With the motor off, place the brush in the large tube. Start the motor and work the brush up and down the tube, taking care that the brush does not come out of the tube while the motor is running. Secure the motor before removing the brush from the tube.

g. Remove the large brush, dry, oil, and replace in the box. Disconnect the large shafting, dry, oil, and replace in tube cleaner box. Do not attempt to coil the shafting too tightly. Utilize the full width of the tube cleaner box. Replace the motor and other parts.

h. Remove the 4-inch handhole. Remove the scale accumulation by hand and flush out the scale with a water hose from the bottom head of the evaporator.

i. Replace the handhole, the overflow tube with funnel, the inside feed connection and the manhole cover.

j. Clean the rotameters, manometer and flow control valve.

k. Reassemble the overflow piping.

9B7. Cleaning the heat exchanger. The heat exchanger using ¾-inch o. d. finned tubes should be cleaned as follows:

a. Remove the covers from both ends.

NOTE. Remove the nuts from every stud before attempting to remove the covers. However, it is not necessary to break the gasket joint between the small plate and the inlet end cover. Do not remove the small plate from the inlet end cover except after about 4,000 hours.

b. Connect the tube cleaning motor and flexible shafts as for cleaning the ¾-inch o. d. tubes of the evaporator. (See Figures 9-3 and 9-4.) Connect the water hose with nozzle for the ¾-inch o. d. tubes attached. (See Figure 9-5.)

c. Examine the scaled tubes and select the proper tool.

NOTE. The lower three or four rows of tubes in the exchanger will usually have a hard scale similar to that found in the evaporator tubes. The carbide tipped cutter bit is the best and quickest tool to remove a hard scale and should be used in these tubes.

The upper five or six rows of tubes in the exchanger will usually have a soft slime-like scale. The expanding wire brush will remove this type of scale quite effectively and should be used in these tubes. Both of these attachments should be used at 3,450 rpm. One man should stand by the motor to operate the switch, a second man should clean the tubes, and a third man should handle the water hose.

d. Insert the hose nozzle in the end of heat exchanger tube at the less accessible end and run a small stream of water through the tube. With the proper tool attached, mark off a point on the cable about 49 inches from the end. Start the tube cleaner motor and pass the cleaner through the tube, withdrawing the hose nozzle just before the cleaner reaches the nozzle. Care should be taken to line up the cable with the tube when starting the cleaner tool into the tube.

NOTE. A stream of water must always be flowing through the tubes while cleaning.

CAUTION. Should the bit jam, secure the motor immediately and free the bit. Try cautiously again. If the bit continues to jam, mark the tube and go on to the next one. Clean the marked tubes with the vibrating head or expanding wire brush. Should the cleaning tool fail to turn while the motor is running, the small hexagonal shear coupling is probably broken. Remove the housing from the end of the casing (left-hand thread) and replace the shear coupling (Figure 9-2).

e. Dry, oil, and replace the tube cleaning gear in box.

NOTE. Be certain to disassemble and grease the 9-foot shafting before replacing in the box.

f. Remove the ¾-inch brine overflow pipe connection at the bottom of the exchanger and clean the pipe. Connect to the heat exchanger after cleaning.

g. Clean the end covers of the exchanger and replace, using new gaskets.

9B8. Instructions for resharpening cutter bits. A hone is provided in the tube cleaning box for sharpening the tungsten carbide cutting edge. When the bit cannot be sharpened by the hone, it must be ground. A diamond impregnated or silicon carbide wheel should be used.

a. Each flute of the cutter bits must be ground separately.

b. Grind only on the cutting edges, never on the diameter, noting particularly that the 15° relief angle is maintained.

c. If a wheel is used:

1. Never permit the wheel to become loaded. Keep it clean.

2. Keep the bits in motion while passing the wheel, avoiding any stationary contact.

d. Be certain that the cutting edge of each tungsten carbide bit is indexed and ground identically so that each flute does the same amount of cutting.

9B9. Acid cleaning. Naval vessels employing vapor compression distilling units, particularly submarines, maintain a very limited reserve of distillate. It is therefore important to maintain distiller efficiency at the highest possible level and to assure a minimum of lay-up time for removing the scale deposits from the heat transfer surfaces.

The mechanical method of cleaning is inefficient, time consuming and somewhat damaging to the heat transfer surfaces. As a result, distilling units were generally operated to the point of lowest tolerable capacity, necessitating long and expensive overhaul periods.

In consideration of the foregoing, an acid cleaning method has been adapted for submarine usage.

9B10. Intervals of cleaning. Clean distilling plants with the sodium acid sulphate solution, normally after each 250 hours of operation, or when the steam chest pressure reaches 6 psi.

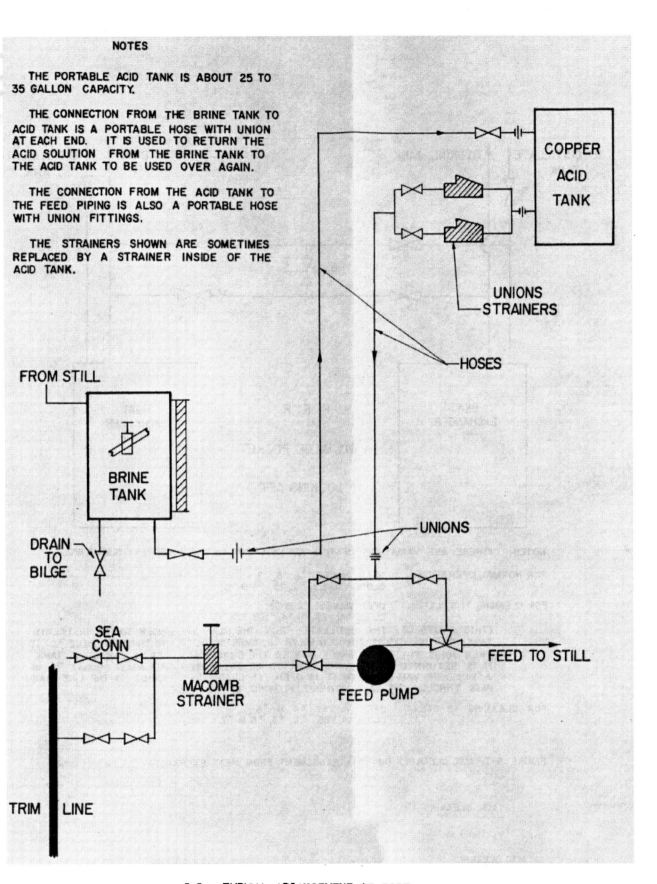

NOTES

THE PORTABLE ACID TANK IS ABOUT 25 TO 35 GALLON CAPACITY.

THE CONNECTION FROM THE BRINE TANK TO ACID TANK IS A PORTABLE HOSE WITH UNION AT EACH END. IT IS USED TO RETURN THE ACID SOLUTION FROM THE BRINE TANK TO THE ACID TANK TO BE USED OVER AGAIN.

THE CONNECTION FROM THE ACID TANK TO THE FEED PIPING IS ALSO A PORTABLE HOSE WITH UNION FITTINGS.

THE STRAINERS SHOWN ARE SOMETIMES REPLACED BY A STRAINER INSIDE OF THE ACID TANK.

COPPER ACID TANK

UNIONS — STRAINERS

HOSES

FROM STILL

BRINE TANK

DRAIN TO BILGE

UNIONS

SEA CONN

MACOMB STRAINER

FEED PUMP

FEED TO STILL

TRIM LINE

9-6   TYPICAL ARRANGEMENT OF PORTABLE ACID CLEANING TANK AND CONNECTIONS TO DISTILLING PLANT.

9B11. Cleaning crew required. One man can efficiently clean one distilling plant in 2 hours time if equipment is kept available and in a good state of readiness.

9B12. Equipment required.

a. One copper or nonferrous metal container of 25–35 gallons capacity, fitted with a bottom discharge line and suitable strainers, valves and a fine mesh screen cover.

b. Suitable hoses for connecting the brine tank to the acid tank and the acid tank to the feed pump. It is suggested that all hose couplings be numbered to insure tight make-up.

c. 50 pounds of sodium acid sulphate (niter cake) for each distilling plant to be cleaned.

9B13. Preparations for cleaning.

a. Fill evaporator as for normal operation, and turn on all heaters.

b. While waiting for unit to heat up, carry out normal prestarting routine, checking:

1. Tightness of belts.
2. Compressor oil level.
3. Bypass valve open.
4. Motor rheostat turned down.
5. On converted units, while cleaning, check open evaporator level safety line stop valve.

c. Make up mixture of sodium acid sulphate and water (salt or fresh), following formula:

$$\text{Sodium acid sulphate (lbs.)} = \text{capacity of unit (gph)} \times 4/5$$

This makes a mixture of about 12 percent strength.

d. Make necessary connections, with hoses to feed pump from acid tank, and from brine tank to acid tank. (See Figure 9–6.)

NOTE. Be sure that the hose from the acid tank to the feed pump is filled with the acid solution and free of air.

e. Line up condensate and brine systems as in Figure 9–7.

9B14. Procedure for cleaning.

a. When unit is ready to start, follow normal starting procedures.

b. When balanced, cut feed rate to about 50 percent normal flow. To maintain distillate balance this will require cutting off heaters.

c. Shift feed pump suction from normal source to acid tank suction line. Secure the normal source.

d. Blow or drain first 20 gallons of brine-condensate mixture to bilge. Afterwards blow all acid-brine-condensate mixture to acid tank. This keeps acid solution at full strength.

e. Maintain steam chest pressure at four psi, using bypass valve.

f. Continue circulating acid-brine-condensate mixture through the unit for 1½ hours.

g. Shift the feed pump suction to the normal source after cleaning period is completed, and discharge all distillate to the bilge, making frequent Kleinschmidt conductivity tests until distillate is acceptable for regular use. One hour's operation should restore maximum purity.

NOTE. If need for distillate is critical, it can be run to the regular storage throughout the cleaning process, provided the Kleinschmidt conductivity tests taken on the distillate is within the specified limits. This will require that the same amount of water (salt or fresh) be added to the mixture to keep it to the correct strength.

NOTE. Should the steam chest pressure remain high after returning to normal operation, the distilling unit has not been properly descaled. In such a case, repeat the cleaning process, using a fresh charge of sodium acid sulphate mixture.

h. Shift the distillate to its regular storage and continue normal operation.

i. When secured, rinse all equipment with fresh water and stow away for future use.

9B15. Safety precautions.

a. Sodium acid sulphate is inert in the dry state. Store in moistureproof containers.

b. It is only mildly acidic when in use and will not harm the skin or clothing. Normal safety precautions should be followed to prevent contact with the eyes or with skin for prolonged periods. Mild irritations will result.

c. Insure that all equipment is kept clean, and if acid container is used as a rag or waste container, clean thoroughly of all oil and waste before using again.

d. Keep valves in systems in good condition, to insure there is no possible contamination of distillate when in normal use.

10

NEW SUBMARINE DISTILLING SYSTEMS

INTRODUCTION

As of the date of revision of this text (Jan. 1955) there are a number of new types of submarines in commission or being built. Fresh water requirements, space availability, and other variable conditions have brought about the installation of several different distilling systems on these submarines.

In Section 6A1 mention is made of these new models. In this chapter, a section is devoted to a brief description of each. Some of them have not yet been fully evaluated under actual operating conditions, and it is possible that some changes will be made. Therefore, no detailed descriptions are attempted in this discussion.

All of these models except the Soloshell employ the vapor compression principle and all are entirely electric. They differ from the Model X-1 (AAA-1) only in capacity, physical size, and small mechanical and operational details. The Soloshell is a steam evaporator operating on the vacuum principle.

A. BADGER MODEL V-1

10A1. General information. This is a vapor compression unit of the same rated capacity and similar in size and appearance to the Model X-1 (or AAA-1) but of modified design.

The Model V-1 was designed to operate under a vacuum of approximately 22 inches of Hg. This meant that the boiling temperature of the sea water feed could be lowered, with a resulting lower rate of scale formation and a softer type of scale deposit. The unit could, as a result, be operated for longer periods before cleaning. Also, since the unit is completely sealed off from the atmosphere, the pressure fluctuations when snorkeling should have no affect on the operation of the unit.

Two of these units were installed on each of the SS563 class submarines. Under actual operating conditions they failed to prove entirely satisfactory and some alterations to the original design were necessary.

The following is a brief description of the original installations, a discussion of some of the problems encountered under actual operating conditions and the alterations made to insure satisfactory operation.

10A2. Description. The distilling unit consists of two main parts, the *evaporator* and the *heat exchanger*. (See Figure 10-1.) The evaporator has a vertical tube steam chest with a vapor separator above the steam chest for separation of liquid particles from the vapor. A 3-lobed vapor compressor, fitted with a bypass valve for starting, is mounted on top of the evaporator. A 12-hp electric motor is mounted on top of the evaporator and drives the compressor.

The heat exchanger, connected to the evaporator by piping, is of the double tube type. Its function is to heat the incoming feed water by absorbing heat from the condensate and the brine overflow. All of these features are similar in construction and location to the Model X-1.

10A3. Distilling cycle. The cycle is started by two horizontally placed electric heaters which heat the distilled water in the bottom of the steam chest. Heat from the distilled water is transferred through the tubes of the *steam chest* to the *feed water* inside of the tubes (after the unit is in operation, the feed water is also preheated in the heat exchanger). The vapor from the boiling feed passes through a *vapor separator* to the *vapor compressor*, where its pressure (and temperature) is raised.

The compressed steam, still under a vacuum relative to the atmospheric pressure, passes from the *compressor* to the *steam chest* where it gives up its latent heat of vaporization to the feed water as the steam condenses.

A distillate trap in the steam chest keeps the level of the distilled water high enough to cover

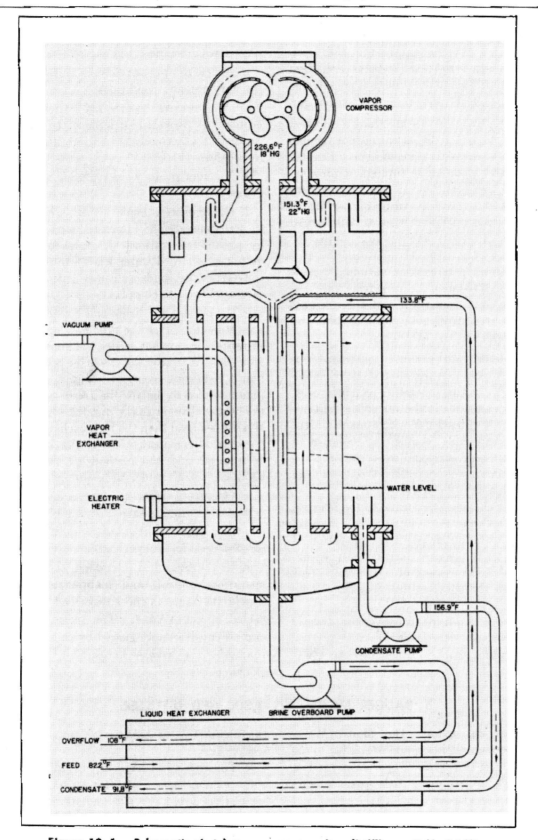

Figure 10—1. Schematic sketch vapor compression distilling unit Model V1.

the two heating elements. These two thermostatically controlled heaters supply the additional heat to the distillate necessary to balance the heat losses. The heat from the distillate is transferred to the incoming feed water in the heat exchanger.

10A4. Pumps. In order to maintain a *vacuum*, a horizontal centrifugal displacement type vacuum pump is used to draw the air and noncondensable gases from the steam chest through a pipe extending into the steam chest. An arrangement of baffles is used to direct the air to this perforated pipe. These noncondensable gases are discharged through the heat exchanger and into the atmosphere.

Since the unit operates on a vacuum, a brine pump is required to pump the brine from the evaporator to the heat exchanger, and a condensate pump is required to remove the distillate and pump it through the heat exchanger.

10A5. Alterations. As previously mentioned, this model did not prove entirely satisfactory as designed. Under actual operating conditions, it was extremely sensitive to the variable conditions encountered. It proved difficult to maintain the vacuum. Considerable trouble was experienced with the compressor seals and when the unit was under a vacuum, it was very difficult to locate and rectify air leaks into the system.

As a result, changes were made to the original installations. Conversion kits were supplied which, after installation, permitted operation of the units under a pressure (similar to the converted Model X–1) instead of a vacuum. This conversion greatly increased the capacity of these units.

In order to accomplish this conversion, several mechanical changes were made:

a. The vacuum pump, no longer necessary, was eliminated.

b. The vacuum operated compressor was replaced with one designed for pressure operation.

c. A new compressor drive was installed to suit the new pressure conditions.

d. A pressure controlled (pressure-static) switch was provided to replace the temperature controlled (thermostatic) switch for control of the heaters.

e. Vacuum gages were replaced with pressure gages.

f. Changes were made in lines and flowmeters to accommodate the increased capacity obtained by pressure operation. (Before conversion the output of distilled water was 50 to 55 gph; after conversion the condensate rate with a clean unit increased to 75 to 80 gph.)

g. At present the brine and condensate pumps are retained. Since the unit now operates under pressure, they are not needed to remove the liquids from the evaporator, but the brine pump is used to pump the brine overboard, and the condensate pump is used to deliver the fresh water through the heat exchanger to the distillate tank, which is at a higher level than the heat exchanger. A proposed rearrangement, whereby the distillate tank is lowered and the method of brine disposal changed, would render these pumps unnecessary.

h. Operating under pressure, a desuperheating system became necessary. A line equipped with an orifice from the distillate pump to the compressor provides the desuperheating water.

With the described alteration, the methods of operation, control, and maintenance are very nearly the same as those described for the converted Model AAA–1. The increased capacity and other advantages gained by conversion, more than offset the decrease in operating time between cleanings.

B. BADGER MODEL WS–1,300 GPD DISTILLER

10B1. General description. The Model WS–1 vapor compression distilling unit is similar to the Model X–1 in its principles of operation. It is a small compact unit requiring little space, thus its selection for use aboard the T-Class of submarines. One of these units is installed on each of this class vessel.

The distilling unit consists of three main parts;

the *evaporator*, the *heat exchanger*, and the *vapor compressor*.

a. The evaporator has a vertical tube type steam chest with a vapor separator space above it for separating liquid particles out of the vapor. A motor-driven water sealed type vapor compressor, fitted with a bypass valve for starting, is mounted in the upper section of the evaporator.

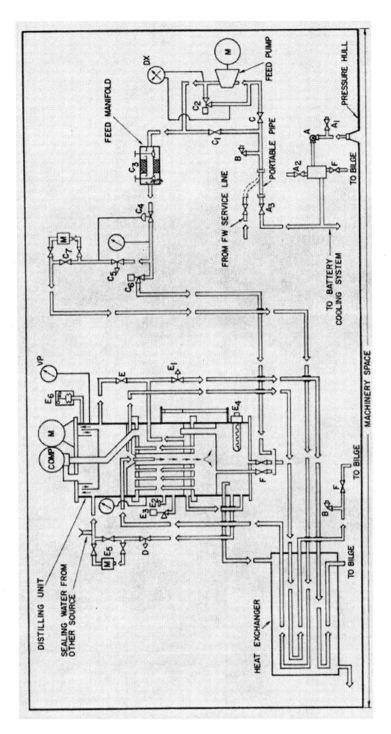

DISTILLING SYSTEM

A	SEA V, SW SUPPLY BATT COOLING & DIST SYS
A_1	HOSE V, SEA BOX BLOW
A_2	STOP V, STRAINER VENT
A_3	STOP V, SUCT FROM SEA
B	HOSE V, CONN. FOR ACID CLEANING
C	STOP V, FEED PUMP SUCT
C_1	STOP V, FEED PUMP BYPASS
C_2	RELIEF V, SET AT 14 PSI
C_3	MAN. V, STRAINER SELECTION
C_4	REGULATING V, SW (OR FW) TO DISTILLER
C_5	NEEDLE V, FLOW CONTROL
C_6	RELIEF V, SET AT 15 PSI
C_7	STOP VALVES, FEED ROTAMETER SUPPLY & BYPASS
D	NEEDLE V, WATER TO COMPRESSOR SEAL
E	STOP V, COMPRESSOR BYPASS
E_1	NEEDLE V, EVAPORATOR VENT
E_2	FILLING CONNECTION
E_3	RELIEF V, SET AT
E_4	ELECTRIC HEATER
E_5	STOP VALVES, COMPRESSOR WATER SEAL
	ROTAMETER SUPPLY & BYPASS
E_6	PRESSURE OPERATED HEATER CONTROL SWITCH
F	STOP V, DRAIN

SCHEMATIC
WS-1 DISTILLING SYSTEM

Figure 10-2.

The lower portion is fitted with a boiler section in which two 2,000-watt electric heaters are mounted horizontally. One of the two heaters is controlled automatically to maintain proper evaporator operating pressures.

These heating elements project into the lower part of the boiler section, which acts as a reservoir for the distillate. With this arrangement, the heaters add heat to the distillate instead of directly to the sea water feed. Some of this added heat is transmitted to the feed water in the upper part of the boiler section through the plating separating the two liquids, and some of the heat is given up to the cool feed water in the heat exchanger.

b. The heat exchanger is the horizontal double tube type, with all features of the heat exchangers used with Model X–1.

c. The vapor compressor is the liquid sealing ring type, installed in the evaporator. Motive power is supplied by a 5-hp motor, with a belt drive, mounted on the evaporator casing.

1082. Cycle. (See Figure 10–2.) Feed is supplied by a feed pump through the rate-of-flow controller (feed pressure regulator), feed control valve, and feed rotameter to the heat exchanger, where it is preheated by the hot distillate. Feed water leaves the heat exchanger and goes to the evaporator, where it is fed into the central downtake tube. It then picks up heat from the distillate and steam in the steam chest as it rises up through the tubes.

Vapor, from the boiling feed at the top of the steam chest, passes up through the vapor separator where any entrained liquid particles will be separated from the vapor. The compressor takes a suction from the separator and discharges down to the steam chest where the steam, on the outside of the tubes, gives up its latent heat to the incoming feed inside the tubes, as the steam condenses. Every pound of steam that condenses generates a pound of vapor from the feed water for the compressor suction.

The distillate then flows down the distillate return pipe to the boiler section where it is drawn off through the heat exchanger to storage. The condensate discharge line is at such a height as to keep the heaters in the boiler section covered continuously.

These heaters start the operation of the unit by heating the initial distillate, which in turn, heats the cold sea water feed above it to its boiling point and generates the steam to start the vapor compression cycle. During operation, the electric heaters supply additional heat so that a sufficiently high overflow rate can be maintained to retard the formation of scale and balance the heat losses, and so that the proper operating pressure can be maintained in the unit. One of these heaters is controlled, during the operation, by a pressure operated switch to automatically maintain the proper balance.

The hot distillate flows from the boiler section, through the heat exchanger, where it gives up heat to the incoming sea water. It then flows from the heat exchanger to a suitable distillate collecting tank, here it can be tested and transferred to the ship's fresh water stowage tanks.

The brine overflow in the upper section of the steam chest is drawn off through a funnel and brine overflow line and passed through the heat exchanger to the bilge. In the heat exchanger, the brine gives up much of its heat to the sea water feed.

Air and noncondensable gases are directed by a system of baffles to a vent line in the steam chest. These noncondensable gases are passed through the heat exchanger and to atmosphere. The amount of vapor and noncondensable gases vented from the steam chest can be controlled by a needle valve installed in the vent line.

1083. Operation. The distilling plant is balanced and kept in a stable condition by slight adjustments of the feed rate and by the number of electric heaters used. The unit operates on a very sensitive heat balance and operates best when all conditions remain constant. Balance is indicated by a compound gage which indicates the pressure (or vacuum) of the vapor from the boiling feed.

The *temperature* of the sea water feed is a determining factor controlling the amount of heat necessary to hold the compound gage reading at the proper pressure. Under most conditions the automatically operated heater will be sufficient to maintain this pressure. However, if the feed water is very warm, the heat supplied by the compressor might be all that is necessary; or if extremely cold, both heaters, on continuously, might be necessary to maintain the proper operating pressure.

Under the varying conditions usually encountered such as rough seas, snorkeling, etc., the plant is balanced with a compound gage pressure of 6 to 12 inches of water and a feed rate between 24½ gph and 30 gph, depending on the condition of scaling in the unit. As the heating surfaces become scaled, the feed rate should be increased.

During operation, the *compressor discharge pressure* should be between 2 and 4 pounds. The compressor sealing water valve should be adjusted to keep the discharge pressure at a minimum.

If operating properly, this unit will produc about 16 gallons of fresh water per hour (rate capacity is 300 gallons per day) from an input o about 25 gallons per hour of sea water. The dis tillate, made from sea water, will have less tha one part per million of salt.

10B4. Cleaning. The system is designed to b cleaned by an *acid cleaning method* as was de scribed for the Model X–1.

Need for cleaning is indicated by a rise in com pressor discharge pressure. When the compres sor pressure rises to 5¾ pounds the distillin unit must be cleaned.

C. CLEAVER-BROOKS, 300-GPD DISTILLER

10C1. General Information. The Cleaver-Brooks 300-gpd vapor compression distilling unit is a small compact unit, adapted for use aboard the K-Class submarines. One unit of this type is installed on board each boat of this class.

The distilling unit consists of three main sections:

1. *Evaporator*, consisting of the following:

a. Evaporator-condenser section.

b. Vapor head, containing two steam separators.

c. Bottom head and boiler section, containing the two heaters.

2. *Heat exchangers* consisting of two heat exchangers connected in series.

3. *Vapor compressor* with drive.

10C2. Description. (See Figure 10–3.)

1. *Evaporator.*

a. The evaporator-condenser section of this unit performs the same fluctions as the steam chest in the Model X–1 or Model WS–1. Vaporization of the sea water feed inside of the tubes and condensation of the steam around the outside of the tubes, are the main functions.

b. The vapor head section contains two vapor separators, a centrifugal separator, and a cyclone separator. Circuitous passage through the separator baffles causes the vapor passing through these separators to give up any entrained liquid particles. The vapor head is also fitted with a bypass valve which is used when starting or cleaning.

c. The bottom head and boiler section is bolted to the bottom of the shell under the evaporator-

condenser section. The lens-shaped space be tween the lower tube sheet of the evaporator condenser section and the bottom head forms reservoir for the feed water. Below this "fee well" is the boiler, which acts as a reservoir for th distillate. The 2 immersion type heaters projec horizontally into the boiler.

2. *Heat exchangers.*

Two identical heat exchangers of the interlock ing coil type, connected in series, serve the sam purpose as the straight tube type used in othe models. The feed water passes around the coi. and the distillate and brine pass through the coil The feed water is heated and the brine and disti late are cooled in these heat exchangers.

3. *Vapor compressor.*

The vapor compressor is of the centrifugal blad type driven through belts by a 3-hp electric moto:

10C3. Distilling cycle. The cycle is started by tl initial heating of the distillate in the boiler by tl two electric heaters. The boiling distillate, an the vapor from it circulating around the tube of the evaporator-condenser section, heats the fee water inside of the tubes to the boiling point.

This boiling action in the evaporator causes tl feed water from the feed well to percolate upwar through the tubes, some of it being converted t vapor and the remainder returning to the botto section through the downtakes. (A *trough* welde around the upper part of the shell, is connected b 3 channels, or downtakes, to the feed well belo the bottom tube sheet.)

During operation, a portion of this boiling se water feed is continuously discharged as "blov

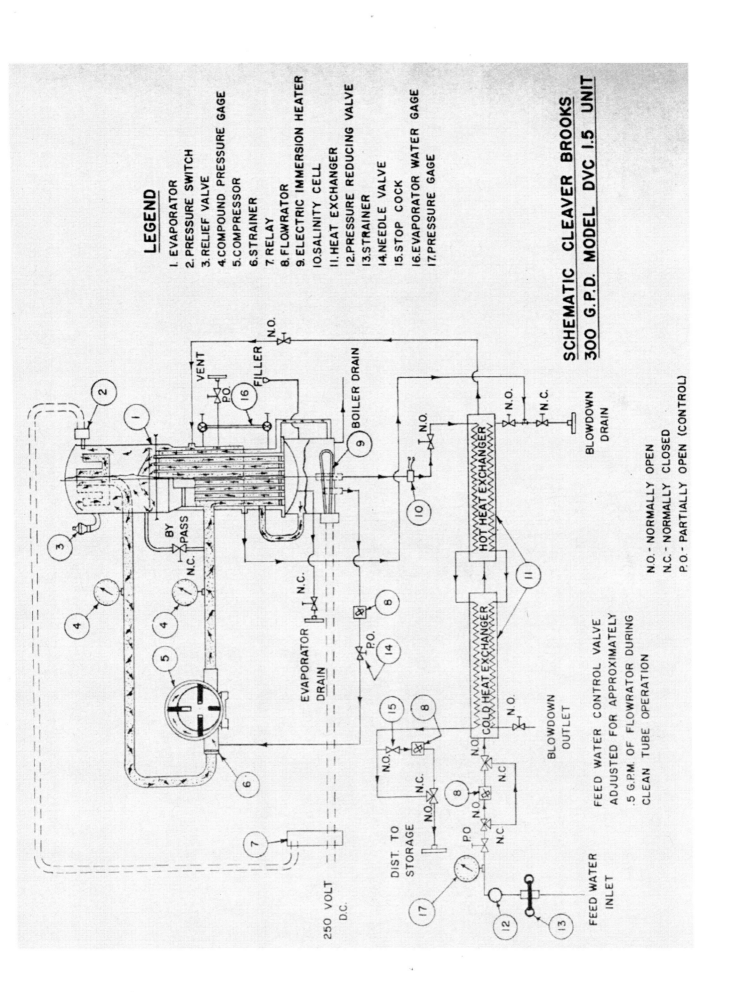

LEGEND

1. EVAPORATOR
2. PRESSURE SWITCH
3. RELIEF VALVE
4. COMPOUND PRESSURE GAGE
5. COMPRESSOR
6. STRAINER
7. RELAY
8. FLOWRATOR
9. ELECTRIC IMMERSION HEATER
10. SALINITY CELL
11. HEAT EXCHANGER
12. PRESSURE REDUCING VALVE
13. STRAINER
14. NEEDLE VALVE
15. STOP COCK
16. EVAPORATOR WATER GAGE
17. PRESSURE GAGE

SCHEMATIC CLEAVER BROOKS
300 G.P.D. MODEL DVC 1.5 UNIT

N.O.- NORMALLY OPEN
N.C.- NORMALLY CLOSED
P.O.- PARTIALLY OPEN (CONTROL)

FEED WATER CONTROL VALVE
ADJUSTED FOR APPROXIMATELY
.5 G.P.M. OF FLOWRATOR DURING
CLEAN TUBE OPERATION

VENT

FILLER

BOILER DRAIN

EVAPORATOR DRAIN

BY PASS

250 VOLT D.C.

DIST. TO STORAGE

BLOWDOWN OUTLET

BLOWDOWN DRAIN

HOT HEAT EXCHANGER

COLD HEAT EXCHANGER

FEED WATER INLET

down" (brine) to prevent too high a salt concentration. This *brine*, or blowdown, is directed through the heat exchangers to recover some of the heat before the brine is discharged as waste. Sea water feed is supplied continuously to the unit to make up for the amount discharged as brine plus the amount converted to vapor.

The *sea water supply* passes through a pressure reducing valve and a flowmeter (flowrator) on its way to the heat exchangers. In the two heat exchangers, the feed receives heat from the brine and from the distillate flowing (counterflow) away from the evaporator.

The *hot feed* from the heat exchangers enters the side of the evaporator-condenser section and flows into the bottom section or feed well through one of the three downtakes. In the feed well, the sea water receives more heat from the boiler section directly below it. Then, as it rises through the tubes, the hot feed receives the latent heat from the condensing steam on the outside of the tubes. Part of the feed is vaporized as it rises through the tubes and part of it returns to the feed well. A portion of the boiling feed drains away through the blowdown outlet to the heat exchangers.

The *vapor*, rising from the boiling feed water passes through the 2 separators in the vapor head and into the compressor suction. Particles of salt water which are removed from the vapor in the separators are collected and drained back to the bottom section.

In the compressor, the pressure of the vapor is raised to about 5 pounds per square inch. This compression also raises the temperature of the steam. The compressed steam from the compressor is forced into the steam chest, where it condenses and gives up its latent heat to the feed water.

The *condensate*, or distillate, drains back to the boiler and then through an overflow outlet in the boiler to the heat exchangers where it imparts heat to the cold feed water before being discharged to stowage tanks. The distillate overflow outlet in the boiler insures that the heaters remain immersed. These heaters remain on when the unit is in operation and would burn out unless covered. During operation, vaporization of part of the distillate is continuous. Some of the distillate is used as a water seal for the compressor, a needle valve and a "flowrator" being used to regulate the amount of distillate flowing to the compressor.

10C4. Operation. This unit produces about 15 gallons of distilled water per hour. Approximately 2 gallons of sea water are required to produce 1 gallon of distillate.

The unit should operate continuously for 500 hours before cleaning is necessary.

10C5. Cleaning.

Indications of need for cleaning are:

1. Rise in compressor discharge pressure above the normal 5 psi.

2. Reduction in distillation rate of more than 10 percent.

3. Reduction in quantity of distillate compared to the amount of power consumed.

There are 2 methods of cleaning used; the *chemical* method, and the *mechanical* method.

The chemical method of scale removal employs a sodium-acid-sulphate solution. One method is very similar to the one described for acid cleaning the Model AAA-1.

Mechanical cleaning; a drill type tube cleaner is run through each tube separately, if a type of scale has been formed which chemical cleaning cannot remove. The coil type heat exchangers cannot be cleaned by this method.

D. VAPOR COMPRESSION DISTILLING UNIT MODEL Y-1

10D1. General description. The Model Y-1 vapor compression distilling unit is entirely electric and rated at 1,000 gallons per day of distilled water. It makes 45 to 50 gallons per hour of distilled water, containing less than one part per million of sea salt, from about 70 gallons per hour of normal sea water and has a constant blowdown (overflow) of 20 to 25 gallons per hour. The temperature of the distilled water (condensate) will be within 15° F. to 30° F. of the sea water feed temperature. The overflow temperature will be about 30° F. to 40° F. above the feed water temperature.

A distilling unit consists of three parts—the *evaporator*, the *heat exchanger*, and the *compressor*. The evaporator has a vertical tube steam chest with a vapor space above it fitted with baffles to separate the liquid from the vapor. Three electric heaters are mounted horizontally in the boiler section, and are automatically controlled to maintain the proper evaporator operating pressure. A three-lobe, positive displacement type compressor is mounted on top of the vapor chamber, and its motive power is supplied by a 7½ horsepower electric motor. The heat exchanger is essentially a horizontal double pipe cooler.

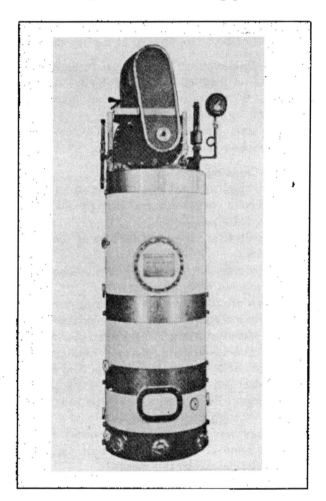

Figure 10-4. Vapor compression distilling unit, Model Y-1.

10D2. Evaporator. The evaporator (see Figure 10-13) consists of four main parts; the *boiler section*, the *vertical steam chest*, the *vapor separator*, and the *vapor compressor*.

The *boiler section* is 22 inches in diameter by 9¼ inches high. It has connections for the three 2,000-watt immersion heaters which are mounted

horizontally in it. It also has a distillate drawoff connection, the lower connection for the gage glass and a ¼-inch I. P. S. drain connection. As this section contains the heaters it must always be filled with distillate when heaters are in operation to prevent them from burning out. During operation of the unit, water in the boiler section is maintained at the boiling point. Hot vapors rise through the ¾-inch I. P. S. vapor pipe to the steam chest. Distillate made in the steam chest flows down through the ¾-inch I. P. S. distillate return pipe to the boiler section. The 1-inch I. P. S. distillate drawoff connection from the boiler section is so located to maintain a level of water high enough to keep the heaters covered with water at all times.

The *vertical steam chest* (see Figure 10-13) is 22 inches in diameter and contains 379 copper nickel tubes ¾-inch o. d. × 16¼ inches long. It has a 4-inch o. d. tube as a central downtake or circulating tube, and an overflow pipe which maintains the proper liquid level in this section. This overflow pipe consists of a funnel and a 1¼-inch I. P. S. tube centered in the central downtake and connected to the shell of the evaporator in the feed water return section. The overflow flows from the unit, passes through the heat exchanger, and discharges into the brine receiver.

The sea water feed boils inside the ¾-inch o. d. tubes at a pressure of between 6 and 12 inches of water, while the steam from the compressor condenses on the outside of the ¾-inch o. d. tubes at approximately three pounds gage pressure. The hot distillate (condensate) flows from the boiler section, through the heat exchanger, and on to the distillate water receiver. Suitable baffles in the steam chest direct the flow of vapor around the tubes, and also direct the noncondensable gases to a central point. A vent line is installed at this point in the steam chest of the evaporator to prevent the noncondensable gases from accumulating. To control the amount of vapor and noncondensable gases vented during the operation of the unit an orifice plate (with ³⁄₆₄-inch orifice) is placed in the flanged joint at the vent outlet of the evaporator.

Besides the connections mentioned above, the steam chest also has the top gage glass connection, and a ¾-inch I. P. S. fill connection. The gage glass allows a visual check of the height

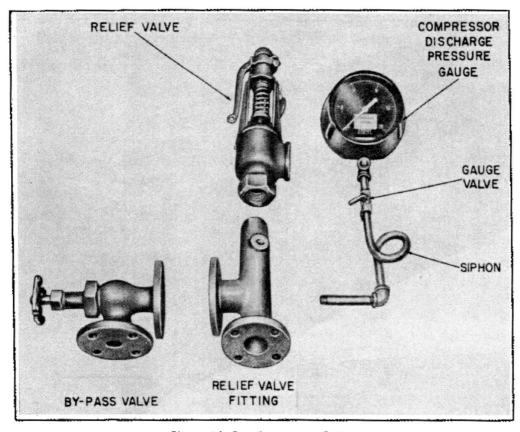

Figure 10–5.   Evaporator fittings.

of the distillate. The fill connection is used to fill the boiling section with enough water to cover the immersion heaters.

Between the steam chest and the boiler section is a feed water return section which contains a 4¼-inch × 8-inch handhole, a 1-inch I. P. S. overflow connection, and a ¾-inch I. P. S. flush and drain connection.

The *vapor separator* (see Figure 10–13) which is fastened by brackets to the top head of the evaporator, consists of a 22-inch shell containing two concentric baffles. This baffle arrangement allows the steam to pass into the compressor but prevents any liquid entrainment from so doing. Small particles of water separated by this arrangement collect on the bottom of the vapor separator and flow into the seal cup. The liquid overflows the seal cup to the boiling sea water, and relatively pure vapor passes on to the suction side of the compressor. The pressure in the evaporator above the boiling sea water is indicated by a compound indicating pressure gage connected to the side of the evaporator. This section also

has connections for the following items located in the outer shell; a ¾-inch I. P. S. sea water feed connection, and a 10-inch manhole.

10D3. Vapor compressor. The *vapor compressor* (see Figure 10–12) is a three-lobe, positive displacement type consisting of two rotors enclosed in a special compact housing designed for bolting on the top head of the evaporator. Each rotor has three helical lobes designed to produce a continuous uniform flow of vapor. The vapor enters the specially designed compressor housing at the bottom and passes upward between the inner and outer walls to the rotor chamber where it fills the spaces between the rotor lobes as they roll apart. This vapor is then carried by the rotors in the spaces between the lobes around the cylindrical sides of the housing producing a pressure at the bottom as the lobes roll together. Clearance is provided between the rotors and the housing to prevent the rotors from touching each other or the surrounding housing.

Vapor is taken from the separator (see Figure 10–12) at a pressure of between six and twelve

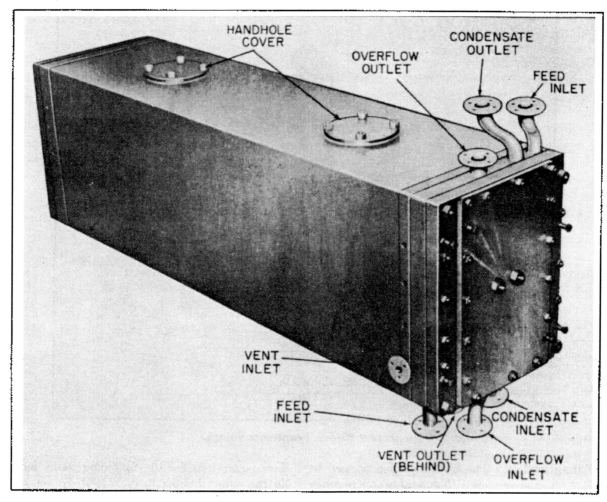

Figure 10–6.   Heat exchanger.

inches of water and is discharged from the compressor at approximately three pounds gage pressure, through a 3-inch i. d. tube within the shell of the evaporator, into the steam chest. A bypass valve (starting valve only) is attached to the top head of the evaporator and is connected to the 3-inch o. d. pipe on the pressure side of the compressor. The bypass valve discharges into the vapor separator on the suction side of the compressor. A relief valve, set at 7½ pounds, is installed on the compressor discharges. A zero to 15 psi pressure gage indicates the compressor discharge pressure. A 7½ horsepower electric motor is mounted on the vapor compressor to supply the motive power.

10D4. Heat exchanger. A double pipe heat exchanger (see Figure 10–14) is connected to the evaporator (see Figure 10–12). The *function* of

the *heat exchanger* is to preheat the incoming feed water, cool the brine overflow and condensate, and condense any vented steam.

The heat exchanger consists of fifty 1¼-inch i. d. tubes, arranged in seven rows of six tubes across, with two rows of four tubes, one at the center and one at the bottom. Inside each 1¼-inch i. d. tube is one ¾-inch o. d. externally finned or wired tube. The condensate flows inside forty-eight of the 1¼-inch i. d. tubes in series, entering hot at the bottom and emerging cool from the top. Steam and noncondensable gases from the steam chest vent flow inside the two remaining 1¼-inch i. d. tubes where the steam is condensed and the gases cooled.

The heat exchanger is divided in such a way that sea water feed flows in series through the ¾-inch o. d. tubes inside 36 of the 1¼-inch i. d.

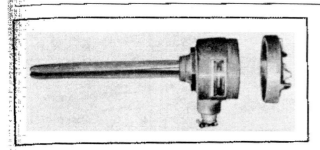

Figure 10–7.   Immersion heater.

tubes, and brine overflow passes in series through the ¾-inch o. d. tubes inside 14 of the 1¼-inch i. d. tubes.

The cold sea water feed enters at the top of the exchanger and after being heated by flowing through 36 of the inner tubes in series, flows from the exchanger to the evaporator (see Figure 10–14).

The hot brine overflow enters the heat exchanger at the bottom and is cooled by flowing through 14 of the inner tubes in series, then leaves the heat exchanger at the top (see Figure 10–14).

The hot condensate from the evaporator enters the heat exchanger at the bottom and flows in series through the annular spaces between 48 of the inner and outer tubes as noted previously. During this circuit, it is alternately cooled by the incoming feed and heated by the brine overflow.

The heat picked up from the brine is transferred again to the feed, and the condensate flows from the top of the exchanger after being cooled to within about 30° F. of the feed temperature.

This arrangement of flows makes it possible to have the sea water feed and the brine overflow inside the small tubes where any scale which forms can be removed easily.

The heat exchanger is insulated by vermiculite enclosed by a light metal shell.

10D5. Electric heaters (Figure 10–7).   The three 2,000-watt electric heaters (see Figure 10–13) are located horizontally and parallel to each other in the boiler section.   They are special chromolox heaters of the tubular hairpin immersion type with the heater section of tubing formed to a triangular shape.   The immersed length is 9½ inches.   The heaters are used on starting the plant to heat the initial cold feed to boiling and to generate the initial steam for compression.   During operation the electric heaters supply additional

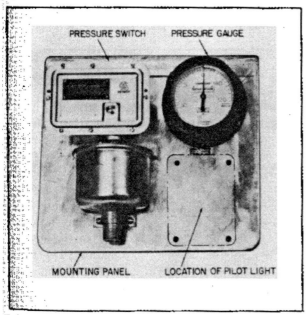

Figure 10–8.   Equipment for evaporator pressure control.

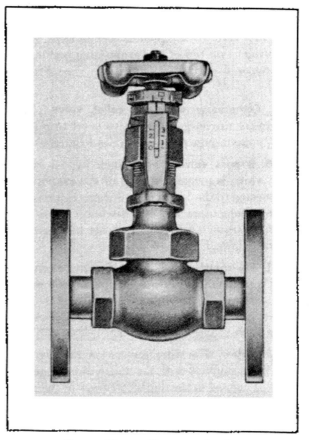

Figure 10–9.   Flo-control valve.

heat so that a sufficiently high overflow rate can
be maintained to retard the formation of scale and
balance the heat losses. Proper inside operating
pressure, indicated by the compound indicating
pressure gage, is held by the automatic control of
these heaters which are turned on and off by a
pressure operated switch set to within the operating pressure limits of the plant.

10D6. Pressure controlled switch (Figure 10–8).
The pressure controlled switch is essentially a
pressure type contact maker, set to break the circuit to the electric heater at a pressure of 12 inches
of water, and make the circuit at a pressure of
6 inches of water. Attachment is on the mounting
plate next to the compound indicating pressure
gage. The mounting plate is located near the top
of the evaporator (see Figure 10–13).

10D7. Compound indicating pressure gage. The
dial of the compound indicating pressure gage is
graduated to indicate zero to 120 inches of water
for pressure, and zero to 15 inches of mercury for
vacuum. (See Figure 10–8.)

10D8. Compressor discharge pressure gage. The
graduations of the compressor discharge pressure
gage are zero to 15 pounds per square inch.
Mounting is on top of the evaporator beside the
compressor discharge relief valve. (See Figure
10–5.)

10D9. Compressor discharge relief valve. The
compressor discharge relief valve is set to relieve
at 7½ pounds gage pressure. (See Figure 10–5.)

10D10. Bypass valve. The 1-inch bypass valve
(V2) which is mounted on top of the evaporator
is connected to the 3-inch i. d. pipe on the pressure
side of the compressor, and discharges into the
vapor separator on the suction side of the compressor. (See Figure 10–5.)

10D11. Flo-control valve. The ½-inch flo-control
valve is provided to control the flow of salt water
feed to the distilling unit. The valve is located
between the feed rotameter and the water regulating valve. (See Figure 10–9.)

10D12. Filter. The filter screens on the two ¾-
inch filters supplied with the unit will be removed
and will be used in the duplex strainer in the feed
water line.

10D13. Brine rotameter. The brine rotameter
measures the flow of brine in gallons per hour.

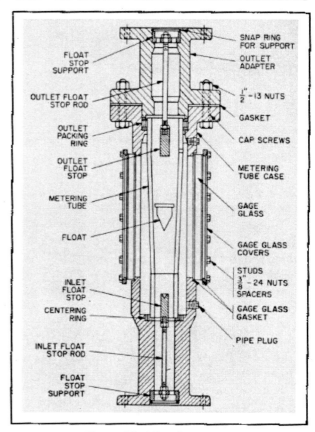

Figure 10–10.   Rotameter.

(See Figure 10–10.) Calibrated capacity = 105
gph.

10D14. Feed rotameter. The feed rotameter
measures the flow of feed water in gallons per

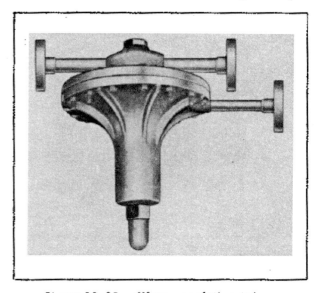

Figure 10–11.   Water regulating valve.

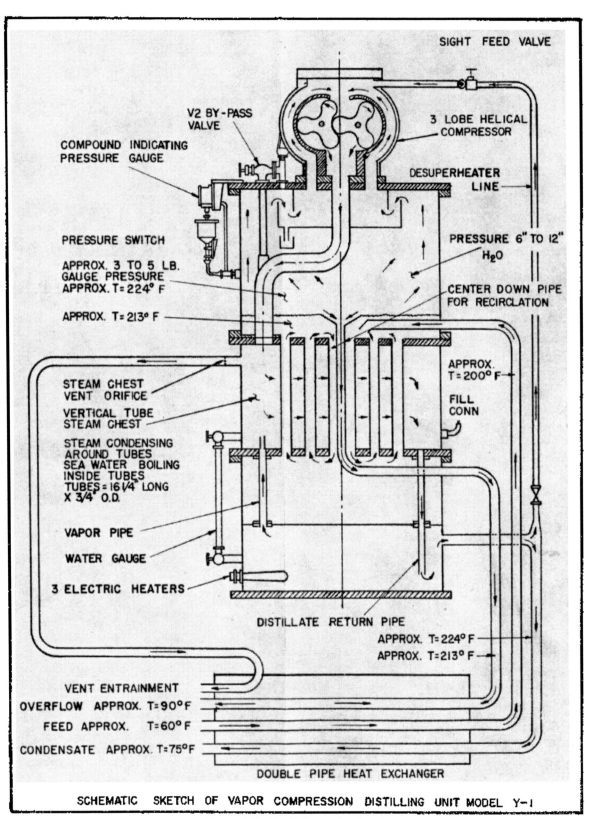

SCHEMATIC SKETCH OF VAPOR COMPRESSION DISTILLING UNIT MODEL Y-1

Figure 10–12. Schematic sketch.

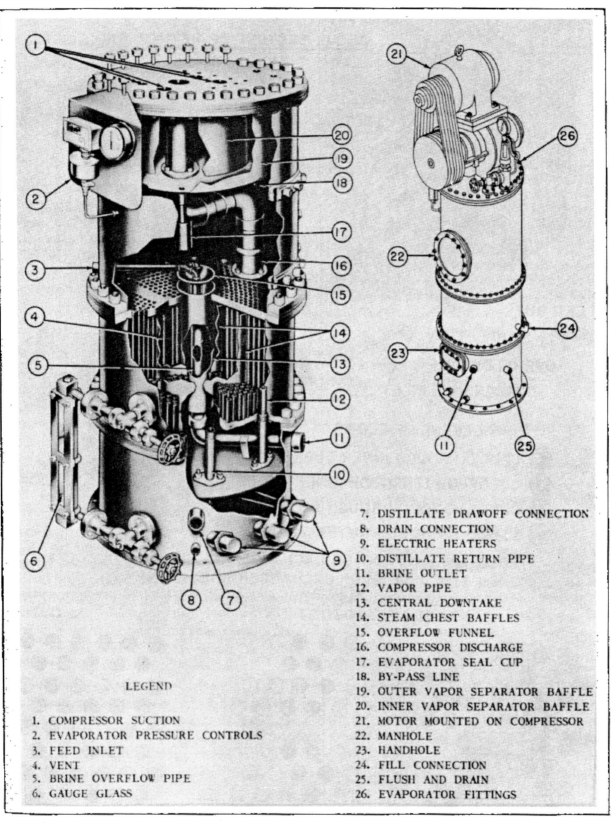

LEGEND

1. COMPRESSOR SUCTION
2. EVAPORATOR PRESSURE CONTROLS
3. FEED INLET
4. VENT
5. BRINE OVERFLOW PIPE
6. GAUGE GLASS

7. DISTILLATE DRAWOFF CONNECTION
8. DRAIN CONNECTION
9. ELECTRIC HEATERS
10. DISTILLATE RETURN PIPE
11. BRINE OUTLET
12. VAPOR PIPE
13. CENTRAL DOWNTAKE
14. STEAM CHEST BAFFLES
15. OVERFLOW FUNNEL
16. COMPRESSOR DISCHARGE
17. EVAPORATOR SEAL CUP
18. BY-PASS LINE
19. OUTER VAPOR SEPARATOR BAFFLE
20. INNER VAPOR SEPARATOR BAFFLE
21. MOTOR MOUNTED ON COMPRESSOR
22. MANHOLE
23. HANDHOLE
24. FILL CONNECTION
25. FLUSH AND DRAIN
26. EVAPORATOR FITTINGS

Figure 10–13.   Evaporator section.

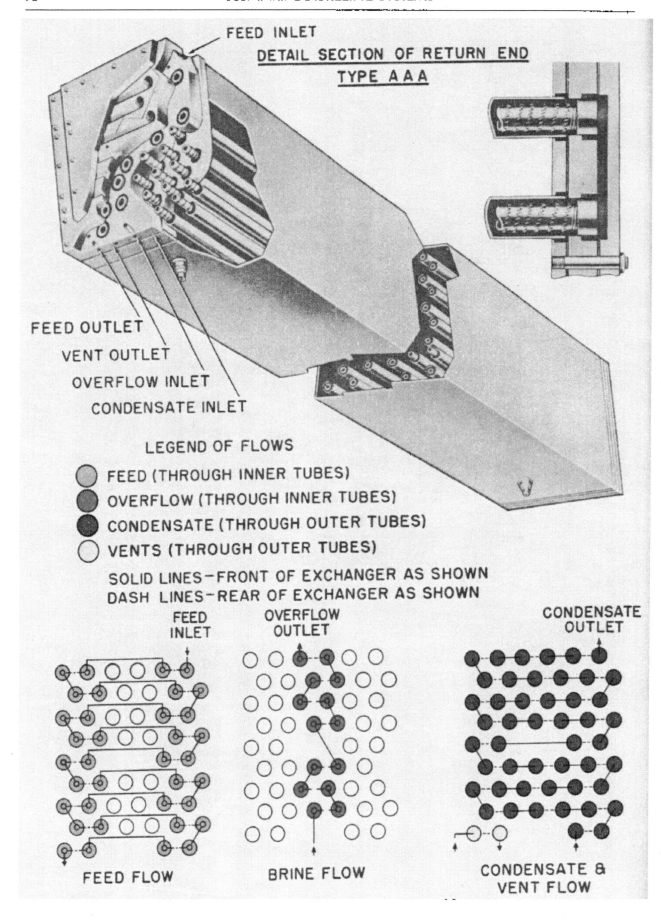

FEED INLET

DETAIL SECTION OF RETURN END
TYPE A A A

FEED OUTLET
VENT OUTLET
OVERFLOW INLET
CONDENSATE INLET

LEGEND OF FLOWS

FEED (THROUGH INNER TUBES)
OVERFLOW (THROUGH INNER TUBES)
CONDENSATE (THROUGH OUTER TUBES)
VENTS (THROUGH OUTER TUBES)

SOLID LINES — FRONT OF EXCHANGER AS SHOWN
DASH LINES — REAR OF EXCHANGER AS SHOWN

FEED
INLET

OVERFLOW
OUTLET

CONDENSATE
OUTLET

FEED FLOW

BRINE FLOW

CONDENSATE &
VENT FLOW

hour. (See Figure 10-10.) Calibrated capacity = 105 gph. Both the feed and brine rotameters are the armored type.

10D15. Water regulating valve. The water regulating valve which keeps the feed flow through the rotameter to the distilling unit at a constant rate is located between the feed rotameter and the filters. (See Figure 10-11.)

10D16. Sight feed valve. A ¼-inch sight feed valve (V3) is located on the desuperheater line to enable the operator to observe the flow of water to the compressor. This line is tapped to the distillate drawoff line just as it leaves the evaporator and provides the water needed for desuperheating purposes.

E. SOLOSHELL TWO EFFECT DISTILLING PLANT

10E1. Introduction. With the application of nuclear power to submarine propulsion there has been installed the first steam evaporator in submarine distilling systems, the Soloshell, double effect, low pressure distilling plant. The principles of operation of this and other types of steam distilling plants can be found in *Naval Machinery* Part III. The discussion herein will be confined solely to the type to be found on submarines with nuclear steam plants.

The principle of operation of the Soloshell is not unlike that of the vapor compression type of distilling plant. Sea water is heated to the point of vaporization, condensed to make fresh water and the resulting brine pumped overboard. The heat source of the vapor compressor is electricity whereas the heat source of the Soloshell is steam.

10E2. General. This distilling plant is of the low pressure, two effect, Soloshell type.

The rated capacity of the two-effect unit is 4,000 gallons per day of condensate, and the overload, clean tube capacity, is 5,200 gallons per day with the chlorine content of the condensate not exceeding one-fourth grain per gallon (produced from sea water). The first effect steam will be at a pressure not exceeding 5-psi gage and the distilling condenser at a vacuum of 26" Hg, the density of the brine overboard discharge not exceeding one and one-half thirty seconds.

The two effect unit consists of a horizontal rectangular shell, within which are incorporated the evaporating units, vapor feed heater, distilling condenser, vapor separators, and water level controllers. A vertical longitudinal wall divides this single shell into first and second effect evaporator shells. The first effect shell contains the first effect evaporator tube nest, vapor separator and vapor feed heater; the second effect shell contains the second effect evaporator tube nest, vapor separator and distilling condenser.

10E3. Principles of operation. For the purpose of explaining the operation of the Soloshell, the distilling plant is divided into seven different circulating systems as follows:

1. Distiller condenser circulating water circuit.
2. Evaporator feed water circuit.
3. Vapor circuit.
4. Fresh water circuit.
5. Brine circuit.
6. Primary steam circuit.
7. Air removal circuit.

To fully understand the operation of the Soloshell and become familiar with the terminology of the various units, the circuits should be followed on the diagrammatic sketch as the text below is read. (See Figure 10-15.)

1. *Distiller condenser circulating water circuit:* The distiller condenser circulating water pump takes a suction from sea and discharges through the condensate cooler and the distilling condenser. A strainer is provided in the pump suction piping. The cooling water makes one pass through the tubes of the condensate cooler and four passes through the tubes of the distiller condenser. The cooling water is then discharged overboard through an orifice which is designed to maintain 8 pounds per square inch back pressure on the distiller condenser tubes and heads.

2. *Evaporator feed water circuit.* The feed water for the evaporator is taken from the distiller condenser circulating water overboard. The orifice installed in the circulating water discharge line (1 above) maintains a minimum back pressure on the evaporator feed line and forces

the evaporator feed through a pressure reducing valve. This valve is provided in the feed line to reduce the high pressure in the circulating water line, which would be encountered under submerged conditions, to a low pressure suitable to the design of the evaporator shell. The feed then passes through the feed heating section of the distilling condenser, and in series, through the air ejector condenser, the flowrator, first effect vapor feed heater, and into the first effect evaporator shell.

The pressure differential between the first and second effect shell permits the second effect feed to be discharged from the first effect shell, through an internal fixed weir-type level control into the second effect shell. Brine is continuously discharged overboard from the second effect evaporator shell through the internal fixed weir-type level controller by the brine discharge pump.

It will be noted that the system is arranged so that the feed water passes from one heater to the next in the order of the temperature levels in the various units, i. e., the heating medium for the feed heating section of the distiller condenser is the vapor produced in the second effect evaporator which is at a lower temperature than the heating medium for the first effect vapor feed heater, etc.

The only exception to this order of heating is that the air ejector condenser is placed early in the series in order that a substantial temperature difference will exist between the condensing steam and the feed water, so that the size of this unit can be reasonably small.

In well designed plants, the evaporator feed water is heated to within about 10° F. of the temperature in the first effect evaporator shell by the series of feed heaters provided for the distilling plant installation. After passing through the last feed heater in the series, the feed water is discharged to the first effect evaporator shell.

3. *Vapor circuit.* The vapor formed in the first effect passes through a vapor separator to remove any entrained moisture carried over, and then to a vapor feed heater. Here it gives up some of its latent heat to the feed water going to the first effect shell. The remaining vapor passes into the second effect tube nest where it condenses causing the brine in the second effect to boil.

During the evaporating process, the vapor is disengaged from the brine at the water surface

and, although the vapor itself is pure, small particles of raw, unevaporated feed water are entrained by, and carried over with, the vapor. The inclusion of these particles of feed water in the vapor generated is known as "priming," or "carryover." These particles of feed water are removed from the vapor by vapor separators of the hook baffle type. They have large vapor areas, and are bolted directly over the vapor inlet connections to the vapor feed heater and distilling condenser. The vapor is forced to change its direction of motion several times in passing around the edges of the baffles or vanes at high velocity. The particles of entrained moisture are entrapped and removed by the hooked shape edges of the baffles. All moisture collecting hooks and baffles are inclined to provide for satisfactory drainage. Drainpipes leading below the surface of the water are provided for discharging the separated moisture as far away as possible from the tube nest in the evaporator shell.

After passing through the vapor separator on its way to the second effect tube nest, the vapor generated in the first effect passes through the first effect vapor feed water heater, where part of the vapor is condensed giving up its latent heat of vaporization to the feed water passing through the tubes of the heater. Vapor feed heaters are shell-and-tube type heat exchangers.

4. *Fresh water circuit.* The condensate formed by the condensation of the first effect vapor in the second effect tube nest is combined with the condensate from the distiller condenser. This combined total of the condensed vapors is routed through a shell-and-tube type heat exchanger called a condensate cooler, where some of the heat remaining in the condensate is transferred to the circulating water on its way to the distiller condenser. By virtue of the different pressures (and boiling points) within the second effect coils and the distiller, the drain from the two are led to a flash chamber. When the second effect drains reach the lower pressure of the flash chamber, part of the hot water will flash into steam and be vented into the distiller condenser where it is finally condensed. A float controlled drain regulator is provided in the second effect drain to maintain a water seal. The distiller condensate pump (a centrifugal type) takes suction from the flash chamber, raises the pressure of the condensate to

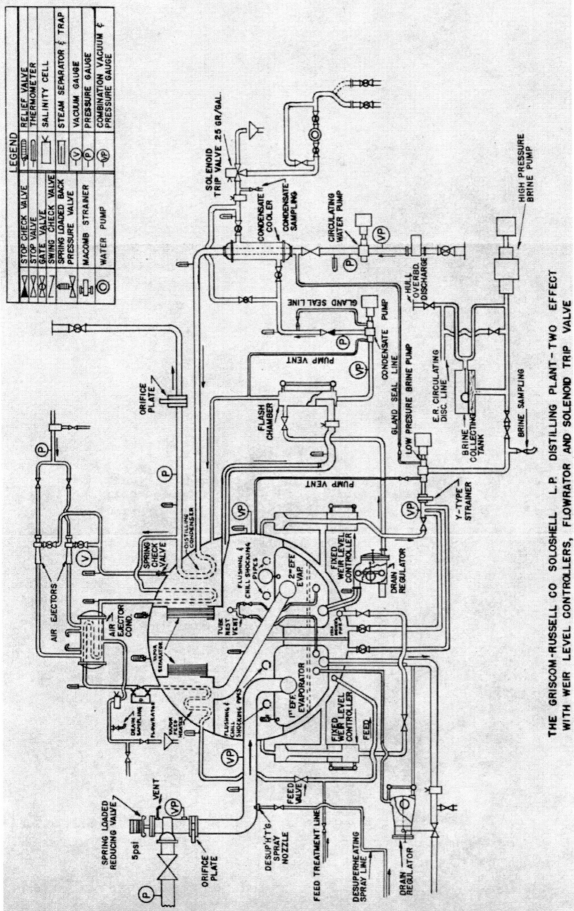

THE GRISCOM-RUSSELL CO SOLOSHELL L.P. DISTILLING PLANT—TWO EFFECT
WITH WEIR LEVEL CONTROLLERS, FLOWRATOR AND SOLENOID TRIP VALVE

Figure 10-15.

a few pounds above atmospheric pressure, discharges to the condensate cooler and delivers it to a solenoid valve. The solenoid valve is so wired that flow can be directed to the ship's tanks only when the solenoid is energized. An increase in salinity to more than 0.25 grains per gallon de-energizes the solenoid and thus trips the valve to the bilge. This arrangement makes it impossible to reset the valve to discharge to the ship's tanks until the salinity is below 0.25 grains per gallon and the solenoid is again energized. In the event of a power failure at the panel, the valve will trip and discharge to the bilge.

5. *Brine circuit.* Fixed weir-type level controllers are installed in each shell. These consist of a weir pipe, open at the top, connected to a weir well at the bottom of the shell. All of the feed water in excess of that which is evaporated spills over the weir pipe and into the weir well and out of the shell. After being partially evaporated in the first effect evaporator shell, the density or salinity of the feed water is increased and it is then referred to as brine to distinguish it from sea water. When sufficient room is not available beneath the distilling plant for the full loop seal, as is the case in submarine installations, a short loop is installed with a valve for controlling the flow. In order to insure proper operation of these overflow weirs in the absence of a full loop seal, a water level must be maintained in the gage glass on the first effect weir well. This is accomplished by hand regulating the valve between the first effect weir well and the second effect shell. Although this procedure still involves some hand regulation, control is much easier because a level anywhere in the gage glass is satisfactory. Also, once the proper valve setting has been obtained with the plant operating at full capacity, it may be left in that position and not disturbed when starting or securing the plant.

It is not necessary to maintain a water level in the weir well between the second effect shell and the brine pump. This level may be anywhere in the glass or out of sight below it. However when the gage glass becomes completely flooded, a stoppage or reduction in flow of brine overboard due to improper operation of the brine pump or other difficulty is indicated. When the overflow weir-type level controls are provided no attempt should be made to regulate the brine pump dis-

charge valve. This valve is left in a fixed open position so that the pump is able to discharge whatever amount of brine overflows the second effect weir pipe. In order to increase the flow of brine overboard and thus reduce the brine density it is merely necessary to increase the flow of feed to the first effect evaporator.

On submarine installations there are two brine pumps provided; a low pressure pump capable of discharging the brine overboard when operating the plant while surfaced or at depths down to periscope depth, and a high pressure pump which is used in series with the low pressure pump when operating the plant at depths below periscope depth.

When operating the low pressure pump alone, the discharge is led to the engine room circulating water discharge line. When operating the high pressure pump in series with the low pressure pump, the discharge of the low pressure pump is directed to a brine collecting tank in which there is a ball float. The ball float operates a valve in the discharge line of the high pressure pump. Thus when the water level in the brine collecting tank has reached a predetermined height the discharge valve of the high pressure pump is opened and the high pressure pump then takes a suction on the tank and the discharge line of the low pressure pump. It is evident then, that the ball float operated high pressure pump discharge valve prevents the high pressure pump from taking a suction on the low pressure pump discharge line which would exceed the gallon per minute discharge rate of the low pressure pump.

The first and second effect shell drains are also connected to the low pressure brine pump through stop valves.

6. *Primary steam circuit.* Main steam is supplied to the first effect evaporator tubes through a spring loaded, 5-psi reducer. An orifice plate is installed below this valve to permit operating with steam in the tubes at a pressure below atmospheric. The thermometer in the steam line between the orifice and the first effect evaporator tube nest will usually indicate superheat, due to the initial condition of the main steam and the throttling action through the reducing valve and the orifice. As this temperature might be too high, resulting in scale formation, the steam tempera-

ture is lowered to the saturation temperature by means of a desuperheating spray line through which condensate is brought back from the discharge side of the engineroom condensate removal system and is sprayed into the incoming steam, removing any superheat present. The condensed main steam, called "first effect drain" is drained to the engineroom condensate collecting system, which is operating under a vacuum. A float controlled drain regulator is provided in the drain line to maintain a water seal. It should be borne in mind that the main steam is the immediate source of all the heat used by the entire plant with the exception of the heat absorbed from the air ejector jet steam.

7. *Air removal circuit.* Air and noncondensable vapors enter the plant mainly with the evaporator feed water in which they are dissolved. As the feed water is heated, the dissolved air is freed and tends to collect in various units of the plant. Air also enters the plant with the incoming steam and through various small leaks at pump glands and imperfect joints. Since the distilling condenser is at the lower end of the heat flow cycle of the distilling plant, the absolute pressure within this unit is lower than that within any other unit of the plant and all air and noncondensable gases, which leak into the system, tend to collect in the condenser. In order that the required vacuum may be maintained, the noncondensable gases must be removed so that they will not insulate the condensing tubes and render the cooling surfaces ineffective.

Air enters the distiller condenser with vapor from the second effect evaporator and flash chamber as well as through a series of vent lines which are led from various units of the plant to the distiller condenser. The proper functioning of these vents is essential to the satisfactory operation of the plant. Two single stage air ejectors having an after condenser common to both are provided for removing the noncondensable vapors and air which accumulate in the distilling condenser. Either of these ejectors is capable of removing the air from the plant under normal conditions of air leakage, the second ejector being available as a spare or for use under abnormal conditions of air leakage.

The air ejector suction piping is connected to the air precooling section of the distilling con-

denser. The main function of the air precooler is to cool and remove all possible water vapor from the air to be handled by the ejectors, thereby reducing the total volume of the gas as much as practicable.

The motive steam is supplied to the air ejectors from the main steam line through a reducing valve which reduces the pressure to about 150 psi.

The steam jet issuing from the nozzle of the air ejector entrains the air and noncondensable vapors from the distiller condenser and raises the pressure of the mixture lightly above atmospheric. This steam is condensed and the air is cooled in the air ejector condenser where the vapor gives up its latent heat to the evaporator feed water passing through the condensing tubes of this unit. The air and noncondensable vapors are vented to the atmosphere. The condensate is returned to the engineroom condensate removal system.

10E4. Starting and securing.

STARTING

1. Open wide all valves in the circulating water circuit from the sea suction to the overboard discharge.

2. Start the circulating pump.

3. Open all air vent cocks on the distilling condenser, vapor feed heater, and air ejector condenser heads until the air is expelled, then shut them.

4. Open the feed valves until the tube nests are fully covered, regulate the second feed valve to maintain the proper water level in the first effect shell.

5. Open the necessary valves in the brine overboard discharge system and start the low pressure brine discharge pump. If below periscope depth, the low pressure pump must be used in series with the high pressure brine discharge pump.

6. Open the second effect evaporator tube nest vent valves wide. The first effect tube nest vent valve should remain shut.

7. Insure that the first effect tube nest and air ejector condenser drain valves to the bilge are open, and that the valves in these drain lines to the ship's condensate return system are shut.

8. Open air suction to the ejector. Open supply steam to the ejector, insuring that full pressure required (stamped on nameplate) is available at the nozzle, and that steam supply is properly drained.

9. Test the salinity of the air ejector condenser

drain. When less than 0.25 grains per gallon, shut bilge drain and open drain to tank.

10. When second effect shell vacuum is about 16 inches, open first effect tube nest steam supply valve wide. Adjust regulating valve to maintain steam pressure of about 5 psi above the orifice. Last effect shell vacuum should continue to increase to 26 inches or more.

11. When condensate discharges from the first effect drain line to the bilge, test for salinity. When satisfactory, shut the bilge discharge line and open valves as necessary to discharge the condensate to the return system and open the first effect tube nest vent valve one full turn.

12. When condensate appears in the second effect drainer, see that drainer discharge valve is open, and adjust second effect tube nest vent valve to the operating position (approximately one turn open).

13. When condensate appears in the flash chamber or distilling condenser hot well, make sure the condensate cooler discharge is directed to the bilge by manually tripping the solenoid actuated valve. Then start the condensate pump.

14. Regulate the first effect feed valve so as to obtain a rate of feed flow of approximately three times the normal distilling plant output. Open the second effect feed valve so as to maintain a level in the first effect weir well gage glass.

15. When the salinity of the condensate leaving the condensate cooler is less than 0.25 grains/gallon, set the solenoid valve to discharge to the ship's tanks.

16. Open and adjust feed treatment injection valve if feed treatment is to be practiced.

17. When the plant has been in full operation for 15 to 20 minutes, determine the rate of distilled water production by means of the meter in the condensate cooler discharge line. The rate of production may be increased or decreased through a small range by increasing the steam pressure above the orifice.

18. When the desired rate of output has been set, determine the density of the evaporator feed, then adjust the evaporator feed valve to obtain a rate of flow in accordance with the table below. The rate of feed flow will be indicated by the flowrator in the feed line.

Feed Density (32^{nds})	½	¾	1	1⅛	1¼
Ratio of Feed to Fresh Water Output	1.5	2	3	4	6

19. After the plant has been in operation about an hour, and occasionally thereafter, check the density of the brine pump discharge, and adjust the first effect feed valve as necessary to maintain a brine density of 1½ thirty-seconds. The brine density is reduced by increasing the rate of feed, and increased by reducing the rate of feed.

10E5. Securing.

1. Shut steam supply to first effect tube nest.

2. Shut the first effect tube nest drain to return system and open drains to bilge.

3. Shut first effect tube nest vent valve.

4. Shut air suction and steam supply valves to air ejector.

5. Open second effect tube nest vent valve wide.

6. Secure the condensate pump.

7. Continue operation of circulating water and brine overboard discharge pumps for 10 minutes or longer to cool all parts of the distilling plant.

8. Secure the brine overboard pump.

9. When both tube nests are fully covered with water, secure the circulating pump.

10. Shut feed valve to the first effect and to the second effect.

11. Shut the suction and overboard sea chests.

12. Shut air ejector and condenser drain lines to return system and open drains to bilge.

13. Trip the solenoid actuated valve to discharge to the bilge.

10E6. General notes.

1. Pumps must not be run dry. Before starting any pump, make certain that the suction, vent, and gland seal valves are open, and that the pump casing is full of water. On centrifugal pumps, it is preferable to leave the discharge valve closed until after the pump has been started.

2. It is permissible to run a centrifugal pump with the discharge valve shut for periods of 15 to 20 minutes.

10E7. Feed and brine density.
The salt content of sea water is measured in thirty-seconds, and is called its *density*. Thus, sea water is said to have a density of $\frac{1}{32}$ if a 32-pound sample contains 1 pound of salts. Sea water feed is partially boiled off in the distilling plant, and the remaining brine which is discharged overboard has a higher "density" than the initial feed. For best results, the brine density must be held constant at 1½ thirty-seconds. A higher density will result in more scale throughout the plant, while a lower density

results in a needless waste of heat because of the unnecessarily large amount of brine discharged overboard. The brine (or feed) density is measured by salinometers which are calibrated to read directly in thirty-seconds. Salinometers are not to be confused with electrical salinity indicators which measure the salt content of the distillate.

A suitable salinometer must be available for each distilling plant. It should be calibrated for temperatures of 110°, 115°, 120°, and 125° F. If the salinometer is misplaced or lost, a new one should be procured immediately.

With the overflow weir-type level controllers the brine density is maintained at the appropriate value of 1½ thirty-seconds by regulating the feed valve to the first effect evaporator.

No attempt should be made to regulate the brine pump discharge valve. This valve is left in a fixed open position so that the pump is able to discharge whatever amount of brine overflows the second effect weir pipe. In order to increase the flow of brine overboard, and thus reduce the brine density, it is merely necessary to increase the flow of feed to the first effect evaporator.

Samples of brine are usually obtained through a sampling cock at the brine pump discharge. It is important to obtain a sample truly representative of the brine in the last effect shell. The temperature of the sample drawn into the sampling pot should agree closely with the reading of the thermometer on the last effect shell. A difference of more than 3° or 4° usually indicates faulty operation of the brine pump, or dilution of the brine between the last effect shell and the sampling cock.

If the pump gland is located on the same side of the pump casing as the pump inlet, the brine may be diluted by sealing water. In such cases it may be possible to obtain a correct sample by closing the valve in the gland sealing line temporarily. Some installations have been made with a brine diluting line connected from the circulating pump discharge to the brine pump suction to improve the operation of the pump. This line is not necessary, and, unless the flow through it is very carefully adjusted, the flow of brine from the last effect shell to the brine pump may be stopped altogether.

A true sample can always be obtained by means of a vacuum test pot connected to the last effect shell. Such a sampling pot is not as convenient as a petcock at the brine pump discharge, but is recommended where the danger of dilution exists because of the type of pump used, because of the presence of a brine diluting line, or because drain lines from other effects (besides the last) are connected to the brine pump.

The amount of brine which must be discharged overboard in order to maintain a constant last effect shell density of 1½ thirty-seconds varies through a wide range, depending on the density of the initial feed. Feed density is not constant. It varies from less than 1 to more than 1.2 thirty-seconds in open oceans, and through an even greater range when inland seas (such as the Red Sea) and sheltered bays are considered. The higher values are usually found in tropical waters, and the lower values in northern waters.

The amount of brine to be discharged overboard for each pound of distillate is given by the following term:

$$\frac{f}{(1.5 - f)}$$

where f is initial feed density in thirty-seconds. Thus for an initial density of 1 thirty-seconds, two pounds of brine must be discharged overboard for every pound of distillate; for an initial density of 1¼ thirty-seconds, five pounds must be discharged, etc. It is evident, therefore, that a fixed quantity of feed water will not result in a constant brine density of 1½ thirty-seconds in the last effect shell. It is essential that the brine density be checked at hourly intervals, and that the brine regulating feed control valve be adjusted as necessary. The amount of feed required in order to maintain a brine density of 1½ thirty-seconds in the last effect is given by the following expression:

$$\frac{1.5}{(1.5 - f)} \times \text{distillate in gal/min}$$

where f again is the initial feed density in thirty-seconds. Since rotameters are usually calibrated in gallons per minute, the distillate must also be in gallons per minute. Thus for a plant producing 10 gals/min of distillate, feed flow required when the initial density is 1 thirty-seconds is 30 gals/min; feed flow required when the initial density is 1¼ thirty-seconds is 60 gals/min, etc.

Feed samples for density test may be obtained from the vent or drain connections on the distilling condenser or air ejector condenser heads at a temperature within the range of the salinometer.

When using a flowrator to regulate the feed rate, brine samples should be obtained and the density checked by the salinometer at regular intervals to prevent possibility of excessive density because of incorrect readings of the flowmeter.

10E8. Scale. The character and amount of scale deposited on the tube surfaces will depend not only upon proper operation in accordance with the manufacturer's instructions, but also upon the quality of the feed water. In low pressure distilling plants, scale results primarily from calcium carbonate and other minor constituents of sea water. The ratio of these minor constituents to the total solids in sea water is not always the same. Hence, it does not follow that two waters having the same density (same total solids) will necessarily result in the same amount of scale under the same operating conditions. Some bay and harbor waters of very low density may result in far more scale than ocean water. In the oceans, more scale should be expected near coral islands than in other regions even though the feed density may be the same. In open waters, away from the effects of fresh water rivers, coral islands, etc. the feed density is an index of scale forming properties. Scale deposits may be reduced by proper feed treatment. This subject will be taken up later in the text.

When no feed treatment is used, a relatively brittle scale is usually formed. This can be partially removed by chill-shocking the plant daily, thus prolonging the period between shutdowns for cleaning. If the plant is usually secured a part of each day, no other chill-shocking is necessary as the scale will automatically crack off when the plant is started up again. When feed treatment is used, the deposit builds up very slowly, and does not crack as readily as untreated scale. Daily chill-shocking may be beneficial, but a longer interval may be entirely satisfactory. The optimum chill-shocking period must be determined from experience.

10E9. Chill-shocking. Most distilling plants are provided with special flushing pipes over the evaporator tubes to facilitate chill-shocking. The procedure is as follows:

1. Secure the following: Steam supply to the air ejector, the air ejector condenser drain line, the steam supply to the first effect tube nest, the first effect tube nest drain line to the condenser, the feed valve to the first effect, the condensate pump and the brine pump.

2. Open the drain on the bottom of each shell and pump the shells. Shut the drain valves.

3. Open the water supply valve to the internal spray pipes and allow all evaporator tubes to become fully submerged.

4. Shut the water supply to the spray pipes and repeat step number 2.

5. Repeat step number 3. When the tubes are fully submerged, secure the water to the spray pipes, and quickly open the steam valve to the first effect tube nest. The flow of steam will be restricted by the orifice but may be increased for more effective "shocking" by increasing the pressure above the orifice. After the plant has been warmed up, this pressure should be brought back to normal.

6. To put the plant back in operation open the first effect tube nest drain valve to the condenser, supply steam to the air ejectors, open the air ejector condenser drain valve to the drain system, open the feed valve to the first effect and start the brine and condensate pumps.

10E10. Feed treatment. Vacuum type distilling plants can be operated for relatively long periods of time without overhaul and without feed treatment, if properly handled. However, it has been determined that the continuous injection of feed treatment into the first effect shell reduces the deposit on the evaporator tubes and in the brine lines.

Instructions for mixing and injecting a feed treatment mixture can be found in the manufacturer's instruction books.

10E11. Purity of condensate. It is very important that only pure condensate be sent to the ship's fresh water or reserve feed tanks. All distillate having a salt content in excess of a predetermined maximum (usually 0.25 grains per gallon) must be discharged to the bilge. In the case of submarine installations this is done automatically by the solenoid dump valve located on the discharge side of the condensate cooler. The manufacturer's instruction books should be consulted to aid in locating the source of excessive salinity.

10E12. Operation with contaminated feed water.
When operating in regions where the feed water may be contaminated with bacteria, such as in or near rivers, harbors, sheltered bays, etc., it is of the utmost importance to send only distillate of known purity to the ship's tanks as the health of the entire crew depends upon the production of sterile water. It has been determined that *sterile distillate* may be obtained without increasing the pressures and temperatures, providing the total impurities do not exceed 0.25 grains per gallon. This phenomenon occurs naturally when the sun's rays evaporate water free of bacteria at atmospheric temperatures and at low evaporation rates.

Evaporation of water, either at atmospheric pressure or at reduced pressures and temperatures, is a physical separation of water from its dissolved and suspended constituents. Bacteria are larger particles than molecules of salt, and therefore, are also left behind in the brine. The sterilization of water by subjection to high temperature is not necessary if contamination of the distillate by priming or salt water leakage is prevented.

The *salinity* of the distillate may be watched as an index of such priming or leakage and the discarding of all condensate having a saline content of more than 0.25 grains per gallon will protect the men. The solenoid valve for automatically dumping the distillate to the bilge whenever the salinity exceeds the maximum gives added protection. The distillate should also be tested chemically at frequent intervals in order to check the electrical indicator.

The U. S. Public Health Service stresses the importance of not operating the distilling plant in contaminated harbors because of the possibility of contamination of the distillate by distillation of oil or other volatile substances in the feed water. The U. S. Public Health Service further advises against operation of the plant in brackish or fresh contaminated water as the salinity indicator and solenoid valve are of little value in protecting the system against improper operation and carryover of impurities in the feed.

10E13. Materials. The evaporator division wall, shell, shell covers, tube sheets and tube nest covers of all units, evaporator tube support plates and all tubes are copper nickel alloy. All other tube support plates and vapor separators are naval rolled brass. Drain regulator bodies are gun metal. Replaceable zincs are provided in all salt water heads.

The *evaporator tube bundles* consist of ⅝-inch o. d. U-tubes, 0.049-inch wall thickness, expanded at both ends into a tube sheet and supported by a support plate. One tube sheet is bolted to the front of the shell so that the tube nest is free to expand. Support plates are supported on rails in the shell so that the tube nest is free to expand.

The U-tubes are arranged for two passes of the heating steam. The air vents to the second effect shell are taken from the second pass compartment in the tube nest cover through a perforated baffle. Sight glasses are fitted in the front of each evaporator shell for observing the operating condition within. Perforated spray pipes are fitted over the first and second effect tube nests for chill-shocking purposes and are externally connected through the front of the shell.

The *vapor feed heater* is of the straight tube type, having ⅝-inch o. d., 0.049-inch thick tubes expanded into a tube sheet at each end. Expansion of the tubes is permitted through the use of a floating head resting on guides in the vapor feed heater chamber.

The *distilling condenser* consists of two tube bundles, one being the condensing section, consisting of U-tubes; the other a feed heating section, consisting of straight tubes. The condensing section is of the U-tube type having ⅝-inch o. d., 0.065-inch thick tubes expanded at both ends into a tube sheet. A tube support plate supports the U-tube bundle. The feed heating section of the condenser is of the straight tube type, having ⅝-inch o. d., 0.049-inch thick tubes expanded into a tube sheet at each end. Expansion of the tubes is permitted through the use of a floating head resting on guides in the vapor feed heater chamber.

The *air ejectors* are of the single stage type. The air entering the ejector from the evaporator is entrained by the steam jet issuing from the nozzle and is carried through the diffuser, compressed to atmospheric pressure and discharged to the air ejector condenser where its heat is given up to the evaporator feed water. The air ejector condenser is of the straight tube type, having ⅝-inch o. d., 0.049 inch thick tubes expanded into a tube sheet at each end. The cylindrical shell is of copper, and differential thermal expansion between the shell and the tubes is provided for by the flanged ends of the shell. The air ejector steam passes through the shell and the evaporator feed makes several passes through the tubes. The air is discharged to the atmosphere through two vent pipes. The condensate drains from the bottom of the condenser to the drain collecting system.

The *flash chamber* is essentially a receptacle within which the vapor, liberated when the second effect drains are reduced to a pressure and temperature corresponding to the distilling condenser vacuum, is separated from the condensate and directed to the condenser. The total output of the plant is collected within the flash chamber and flows to the condensate pump. The flash chamber is attached to the second effect side of the evaporator shell.

The first and second effect *tube nest drain regulators* are of the style "F" (Griscomb-Russell) internal valve, piston type balance valve design with ball float. The regulators may be locked open in case of derangement. The condensate cooler is of the straight tube type, having ⅝-inch o. d., 0.065-inch thick tubes, expanded into a tube sheet at each end.

The *fixed weir-type level controllers* are located internally and are directly attached to the bottom of the first and second effect evaporator shell. The level controller is self-venting to its respective evaporator shell. Water level within the evaporator is maintained by the fixed weir pipes attached to the level controller body. This water level is indicated by gage glasses likewise fitted to the level controller.

The *flowrator* is located in the feed piping, between the feed water outlet connection on the air ejector condenser and the feed water inlet on the first effect vapor feed heater. It is calibrated in gallons per minute and visually indicates amount of feed water being supplied to the plant.

The *feed reducing valve* is provided to reduce the high pressures which may be encountered under submerged conditions to a low pressure suitable to the design of the evaporator shell, heaters and condenser bundles. For surface operation a back pressure valve is located on the circulating water piping overboard to maintain sufficient back pressure to force the feed through the reducing valve and heaters in the feed line and into the first effect shell.

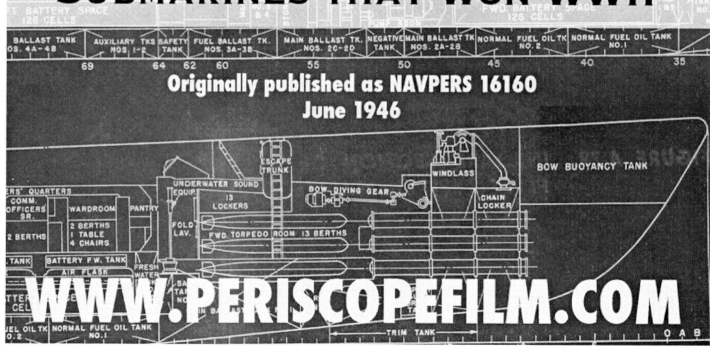

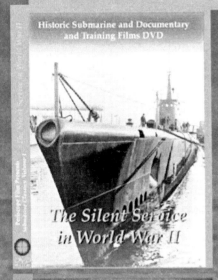

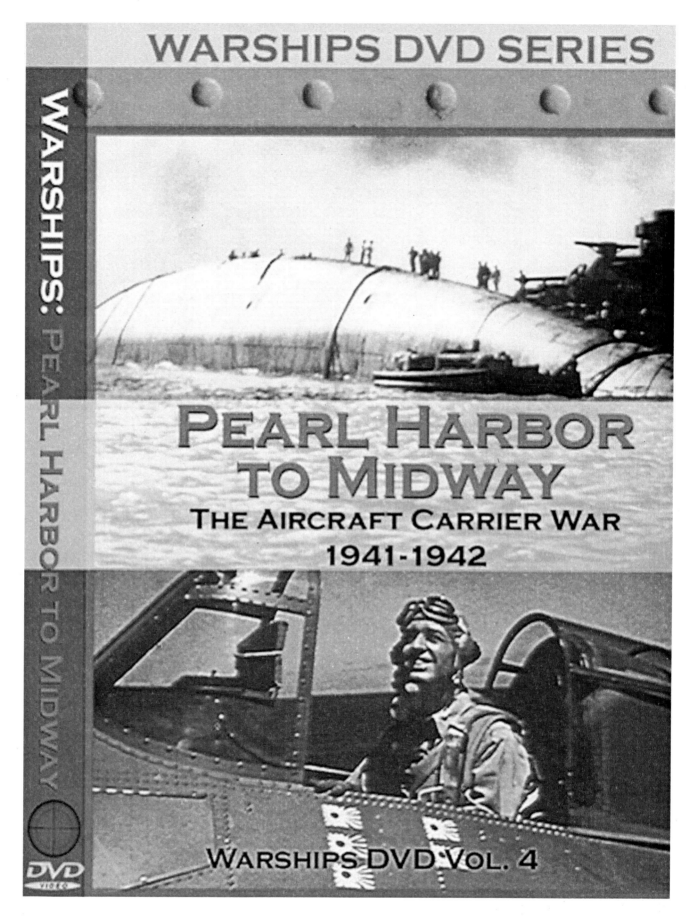

WARSHIPS: CARRIER MISHAPS

AIRCRAFT CARRIER
MISHAPS
SAFETY AND TRAINING FILMS

DVD VIDEO

-PERISCOPEFILM.COM-

NOW AVAILABLE ON DVD!

Features HILARIOUS INSANE and INFAMOUS FILMS from Government Archives!

OFF LIMITS!

OFF LIMITS!

LAUNCH 'EM, THE MAN FROM LOX

(AND OTHER FILMS THE MILITARY DOESN'T WANT YOU TO SEE!)

GOVERNMENT FILMS

DVD

Now Available on DVD!

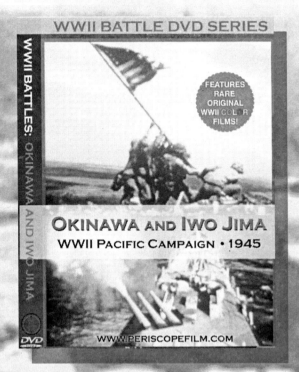
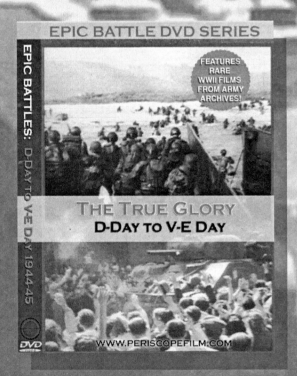

Warships DVD Series

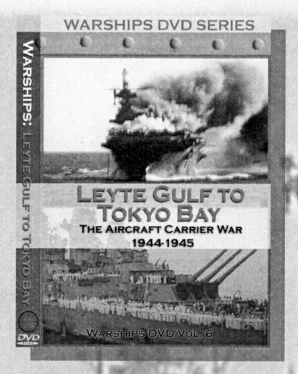
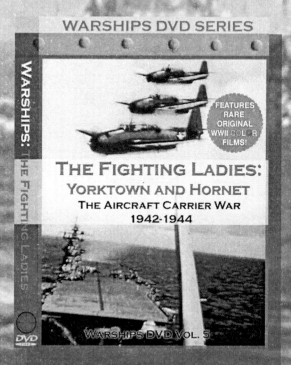

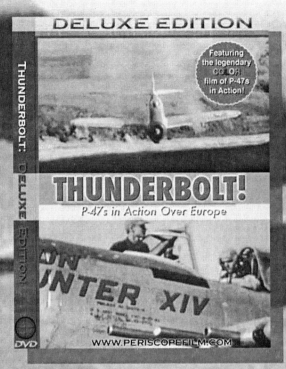
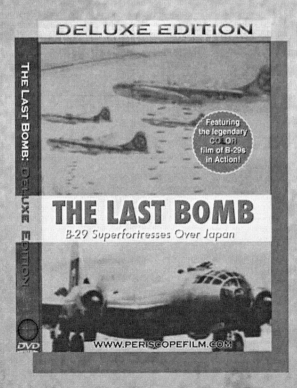
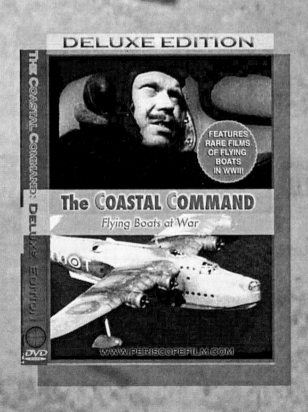

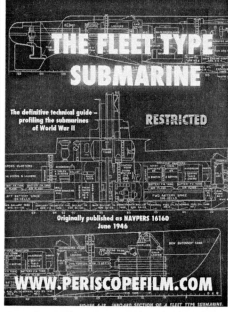

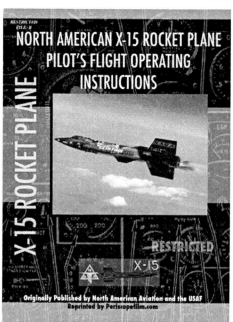
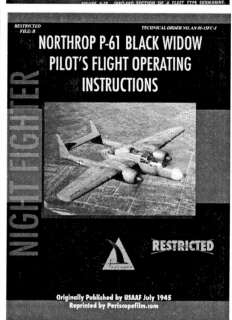
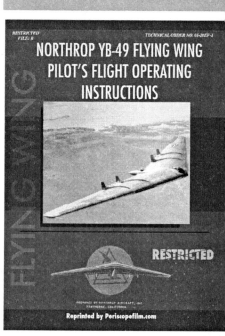
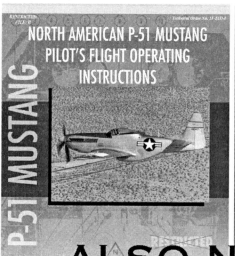

www.PeriscopeFilm.com

ISBN # 978-1-935327-01-1   1-935327-01-1